LEONARD COHEN
ANTHOLOGY

WISE PUBLICATIONS
PART OF THE MUSIC SALES GROUP
London / New York / Paris / Sydney / Copenhagen / Berlin / Madrid / Tokyo

Published by
WISE PUBLICATIONS
14-15 Berners Street, London W1T 3LJ,
United Kingdom.

Exclusive distributors:
MUSIC SALES LIMITED
Distribution Centre,
Newmarket Road, Bury St Edmunds, Suffolk, IP33 3YB,
United Kingdom.
MUSIC SALES PTY LIMITED
20 Resolution Drive, Caringbah, NSW 2229, Australia.

Order No. AM995654
ISBN 978-1-84772-761-9

Compiled by Nick Crispin.
Edited by Jenni Wheeler.
Music arranged by Jack Long.
Music processed by Paul Ewers Music Design.
Cover designed by Michael Bell Design.
Cover photograph by Guido Harari / Contrasto / Eyevine.
Printed in the EU.

Avalanche

Words & Music by Leonard Cohen

Fm
E♭
6fr
Fm
A♭
4fr
I sleep be-neath the gold-en hill.
You who wish to
C7/G
Fm
con-quer pain, you must learn, learn to serve me
D♭
4fr
Gm7♭5/C
well.
1-5.
C
6.
C

Verse 2:
You strike my side by accident
As you go down for gold.
The cripple here that you clothe and feed
Is neither starved nor cold.
He does not ask for your company,
Not at the centre, the centre of the world.

Verse 3:
When I am on a pedestal,
You did not raise me there.
Your laws do not compel me
To kneel grotesque and bare.
I myself am the pedestal
For this ugly hump at which you stare.

Verse 4:
You who wish to conquer pain,
You must learn what makes me kind.
The crumbs of love that you offer me,
They're the crumbs I've left behind.
Your pain is no credential here,
It's just the shadow, shadow of my wound.

Verse 5:
I have begun to long for you,
I who have no creed.
I have begun to ask for you,
I who have no need.
You say you've gone away from me,
But I can feel you when you breathe.

Verse 6:
Do not dress in those rags for me,
I know you are not poor.
You don't love me quite so fiercely now,
When you know that you are not sure.
It is your turn, beloved,
It is your flesh that I wear.

Ballad Of The Absent Mare

Words & Music by Leonard Cohen

D
walk till he finds her, his darl - ing, his stray. But the
A
riv - er's in flood and the roads are a - wash, and the
E
brid - ges break up in the
D
pan - ic of
A
loss.
2. And there's

♩ = 132
A
noth-ing to fol-low, there's no-where to go; she's
(Verses 3-12. see block lyrics)
D
D/C♯
D/B
gone like the sum-mer, gone like the snow. And the
A
crick-ets are break-ing his heart with their song, as the
E
D
A
A/F♯
A/E
day caves in and the night is all wrong.

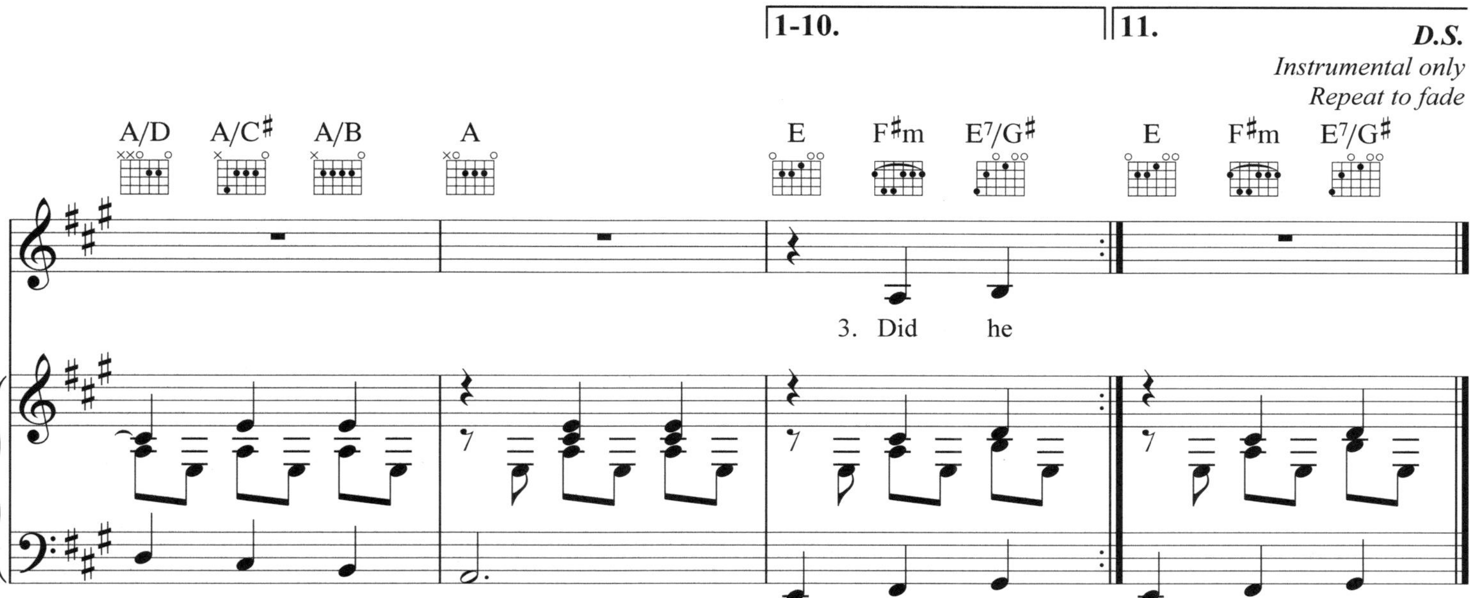

Verse 3:
Did he dream? Was it she who went galloping past
And bent down the fern, broke open the grass
And printed the mud with the iron and the gold
That he nailed to her feet when he was the lord?

Verse 4:
And although she goes grazing a minute away
He tracks her all night, he tracks her all day
Oh, blind to her presence except to compare
His injury here with her punishment there.

Verse 5:
Then at home on a branch in the highest tree
A songbird sings out so suddenly
Ah, the sun is warm and the soft winds ride
On the willow trees by the river side.

Verse 6:
Oh, the world is sweet, the world is wide
And she's there where the light and the darkness divide
And the steam's coming off her, she's huge and she's shy
And she steps on the moon when she paws at the sky.

Verse 7:
And she comes to his hand but she's not really tame
She longs to be lost, he longs for the same
And she'll bolt and she'll plunge through the first open pass
To roll and to feed in the sweet mountain grass.

Verse 8:
Or she'll make a break for the high plateau
Where there's nothing above and there's nothing below
And it's time for the burden, it's time for the whip
Will she walk through the flame, can he shoot from the hip?

Verse 9:
So he binds himself to the galloping mare
And she binds herself to the rider there
And there is no space but there's left and right
And there is no time but there's day and night.

Verse 10:
And he leans on her neck and he whispers low
"Whither thou goest, I will go"
And they turn as one and they head for the plain
No need for the whip, ah, no need for the rein.

Verse 11:
Now the clasp of this union, who fastens it tight?
Who snaps it asunder the very next night?
Some say the rider, some say the mare
Or that love's like the smoke, beyond all repair.

Verse 12:
But my darling says "Leonard, just let it go by
That old silhouette on the great western sky"
So I pick out a tune and they move right along
And they're gone like the smoke and they're gone like this song.

Because Of

Words & Music by Leonard Cohen

Bm
Asus4
G
naked in their different ways,
and they say
"Look at me, Leonard;
D
A
look at me one last time."
Then they
bend over the bed
G
D
A
and cover me up like a baby that is shivering,
like a baby.
(Like a ba-by.)
D/A
F#7/A#
Bm
Because of a few songs, wherein I spoke of their
mystery,
woman have

F♯7/A♯
Bm
Em/B
been exceptionally kind to my old age.
They make a secret place in their busy lives, and they
Bm
Em/B
A
D/A
A7
A
take me there.
They become naked in their different ways, and they say
Sung ("Look at me,
(Spoken) "Look at me,
G
D/A
A
Leo - nard; look at me, Leo - nard; look at me one last
Leo - nard; look at me, Leo - nard; look at me one last
G
D/A
time. Look at me Leo - nard; look at me, Leo - nard; look at me
time. Look at me Leo - nard; look at me, Leo - nard; look at me

A
G
one last time, one last
one last time, one last
D/A
A
D/A
A7
A
G
time.") time.")
(Ooh.)
(Look at me Leo-nard one last
Bm
G
Bm
time.)
(Look at me Leo-nard one last time.)
(Look at me
(Spoken) Look at me
G
Bm
D.S. to fade
Leo-nard; look at me, Leo-nard; look at me
Leo-nard; look at me, Leo-nard; look at me

A Bunch Of Lonesome Heroes

Words & Music by Leonard Cohen

E
E/D
E/C♯
E/B
were smok-ing out a-long the o-pen
the night so dark and thick and
I sing this for the ar-
A
Asus4
A
Asus2
A
Asus2
road.
green.
-my.
A
The night was ver-y dark and thick be-
Well, I guess that these he-roes must al-ways
I sing this for your
Bm
D
-tween them,
live there
child-ren and

E
E/D
E/C♯
E/B
each man be-neath his or - di - nar - y
where you and I have on - ly
for all who do not need
A
Asus4
A
load.
been.
me.
D
D/C♯
D/B
D
"I'd like to tell my
Put out your cig - a - rette,
"I'd like to tell my
A
A/G♯
A/F♯
A/E
sto - ry,"
my love,
sto - ry,"

B
said one of them so young and
you've been a - lone too
said one of them so
E
bold.
long.
bold.
D
"I'd like to tell my
And some of us are ver - y
"Oh yes, I'd like to tell my
A
sto - ry
hun - gry now
sto - - - - - ry,

F♯m
be - fore I turn in - to gold."
to hear what it is you've done that was so wrong.
'cause you know, I feel I'm turn - ing in - - to gold."
1, 2.
E
E7
3.
D.S. Instrumental to fade
E
E7

By The Rivers Dark

Words & Music by Leonard Cohen & Sharon Robinson

D♭maj7
4fr
E♭
6fr
Fm
I lived my life in Ba - by - lon.
Fm
Cm7
3fr
Fm
Cm7
3fr
And I did for - get my ho - ly song,
D♭maj7
4fr
E♭
6fr
Fm
1, 2.
To Coda
and I had no strength in Ba - by - lon.
A♭
4fr
B♭
Fm
By the riv - ers dark where I could not see

D♭
4fr
E♭
6fr
Fm
who was wait - ing there,
who was hunt - ing me.
Fm7
3.
D♭maj7
4fr
E♭
6fr
(And he gave the wind
Fm
D♭maj7
4fr
my wed - ding ring;
and he cir - cled us
E♭/B♭
6fr
C
C7
D.S. al Coda
with ev - 'ry - thing.)

Coda
Cm7
3fr
Fm
Be the truth un - said and the bless - ing gone
D♭maj7
4fr
E♭
6fr
Fm
if I for - get my Ba - by - lon.
A♭m
4fr
B♭6
Fm
I did not know and I could not see
By the riv - ers dark where it all goes on,
D♭
4fr
E♭
6fr
Fm
1.
2.
who was wait - ing there, who was hunt - ing me.
by the riv - ers dark in Ba - by - lon.

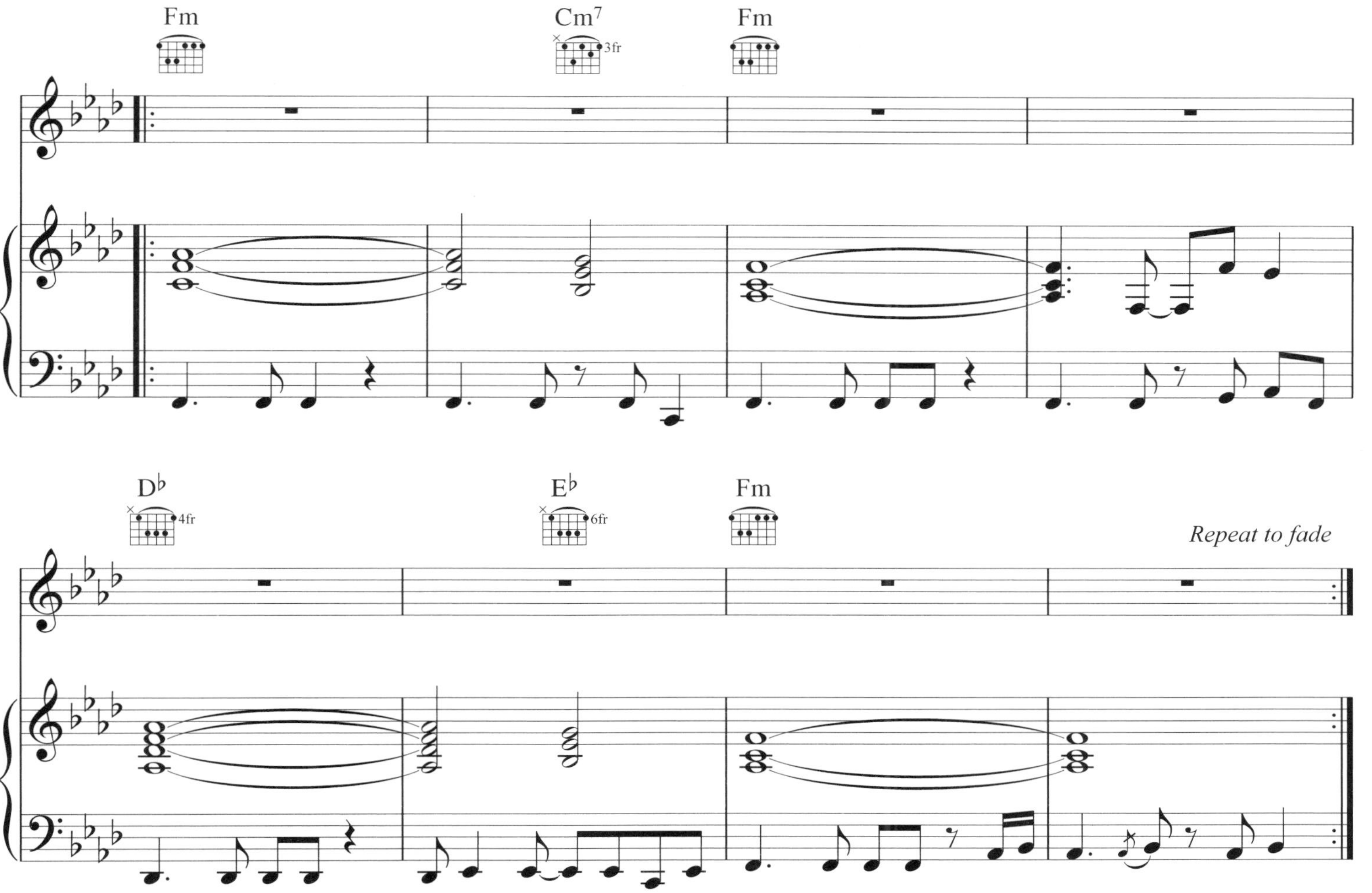

Verse 2:
And he cut my lip and he cut my heart
So I could not drink from the rivers dark
And he covered me and I saw within
My lawless heart and my wedding ring
I did not know and I could not see
Who was waiting there, who was hunting me.

Verse 3:
By the rivers dark I panicked on
I belonged at last to Babylon
Then he struck my heart with a deadly force
And he said, "This heart, it is not yours."

Verse 4:
By the rivers dark in a wounded dawn
I live my life in Babylon
Though I take my song from a withered limb
Both song and tree, they sing for him.

Came So Far For Beauty

Words & Music by Leonard Cohen & John Lissauer

G7
Gaug7
G7
C7
my pa - tience and my fam - 'ly,
1.
(to next strain)
F7
B♭
A
A♭
4fr
my mas - ter - piece un - signed.
2.
F7
poco rit.
B♭
Fine
my mas - ter - piece un - signed.
G7
Gaug7
G7
C7
1. I though I'd be re - ward - ed

F7
B♭
A
A♭
4fr
for such a lone - ly choice.
G7
Gaug7
G7
C7
And sure - ly she would ans - wer
F7
B♭
E♭
6fr
Fm
E♭/G
to such a ver - y hope - less voice.
A♭
4fr
G7
Gaug7
G7
I prac - ticed on my saint - hood,

A♭
G7
Gaug7
G7
I gave to one and all, but the
E♭
B♭/D
Cm
Cm/B♭
ru - mors of my vir - tue, they
A♭
B♭9
E♭
Fm
E♭/G
moved her not at all.
A♭
G7
Gaug7
G7
I changed my style to sil - ver,

Verse 2:
I stormed the old casino
For the money and the flesh.
And I myself decided
What was rotten and what was fresh.

And men to do my bidding,
And broken bones to teach,
The value of my pardon,
The shadow of my reach.

But no, I could not touch her
With such a heavy hand.
Her star beyond my order,
Her nakedness unmanned.

𝄋:
I came so far for beauty,
I left so much behind,
My patience and my family,
My masterpiece unsigned.

The Captain

Words & Music by Leonard Cohen

Csus4 C C7 C7sus4 C7 F C Csus4 C
mand of what? There's no one here, there's only you and me, all the
G G6 G G6 G F C Csus4 C
rest are dead or in re-treat, or with the en-e-my." 2. "Com-
Csus4 C G G6 G F C Csus4 C
-plain, com-plain, that's all you've done ev-er since we lost. If it's
F C Csus4 C G G6 G C Csus4 C
not the Cru-ci-fi-xion, then it's the Hol-o-caust." "May

Verse 3:
"I know that you have suffered, lad
But suffer this awhile:
Whatever makes a soldier sad
Will make a killer smile."
"I'm leaving, Captain, I've got to go
There's blood upon your hand
But tell me, Captain, if you know
Of a decent place to stand."

Verse 4:
"There is no decent place to stand
In a massacre
But if a woman take your hand
Go and stand with her."
"I left a wife in Tennessee
And a baby in Saigon
I risked my life, but not to hear
Some country'n'western song."

Verse 5:
"Ah, but if you cannot raise your love
To a very high degree,
Then you're just the man
I've been thinking of
So come and stand with me."
"Your standing days are done," I cried,
"You'll rally me no more.
I don't even know what side
We fought on, or what for."

Verse 6:
"I'm on the side that's always lost
Against the side of Heaven
I'm on the side of Snake-eyes tossed
Against the side of Seven.
And I've read the Bill of Human Rights
And some of it was true
But there wasn't any burden left
So I'm laying it on you."

Verse 7:
Now the Captain he was dying
But the Captain wasn't hurt
The silver bars were in my hand
I pinned them to my shirt.
Instrumental to fade

Coming Back To You

Words & Music by Leonard Cohen

B♭ C7 F
can't turn the oth - er cheek; but you know that I still
all the bills are due; and the fields they're un - der
4
Dm C B♭ F
love you, it's just that I can't speak. I
lock and key though the rain and the sun come through. And
B♭ F A
looked for you in ev - 'ry - one, and they called me on that too.
spring - time starts, but then it stops in the name of some - thing
B♭ C F C/E Dm Am/C
I lived a - lone, but I was on - ly
new; and all the sen - ses rise a - gainst this
To Coda II

B♭
C7
To Coda I
1.
F
B♭/D
C/E
com - ing back to you.
2. Ah, they're
com - ing back to
2.
F
B♭
C
F
you. And they're hand - ing down my sen - tence now, and I
B♭
B♭/C
F
A
know what I must do.
An - oth - er mile of
B♭
G7
C
N.C.
D.S. al Coda I
si - lence while I'm com - ing back to you.

Verse 3:
There are many in your life
And many still to be
Since you are a shining light
There's many that you'll see
But I have to deal with envy
When you choose the precious few
Who've left their pride on the other side of
Coming back to you.

Verse 4:
Even in your arms I know
I'll never get it right
Even when you bend to give me
Comfort in the night
I've got to have your word on this
Or none of it is true
And all I've said was just instead of
Coming back to you.

Death Of A Ladies' Man

Words & Music by Leonard Cohen & Phil Spector

Gm7
3fr
C
B♭
F
nev - er e - ven knew_ how much I want - ed you,"_ she said._ His
nev - er see such arms_ a - gain in wrest - ling or___ in love."_ And,
G7
mus - cles they were num - bered and his style was ob - se - lete. "Oh
all his vir - tues burn - ing in the smok - y ho - lo - caust, she
1.
To Coda I
To Coda II
ba - by, I have come too late." She knelt be - side his feet.
took un - to her - self most ev - 'ry -
2.
2. "I'll
(2.)-thing her lov - er lost._
(4.) pas - sage to the moon._
(7.)work - ing - class mous - tache._

Dm
3° D.S. al Coda I
3. Now the
8. Now the
mas - ter of this land - scape he was stand - ing there_ at the view_ with a
last time that I saw him, he was try - ing hard_ to get_ a
Gm
3fr
spar - row of St. Fran - cis that he was preach - ing to.___ She
wom - an's ed - u - ca - tion, but he's not a wom - an yet.___ And the
Am
beck - oned to the sen - try of his high re - li - gious mood. She said "I'll
last time that I saw_ her, she was liv - ing with_ some boy_ who

Gm
F♯aug
B♭/F
To Coda III
make a place be - tween my legs, I'll show you sol - i -
gives her soul an emp - ty room and
C/E
C
- tude.
D.S. al Coda I
Coda I
F
B♭
4. He
F
D.S. al Coda II
6. She

Coda II
B♭
F
(6.) ev - 'ry - thing is mine.
Coda III
D.S. al Coda III
B♭/F
rit.
C/E
molto
♩ = 44
7. He
(8.) gives her bod-y joy.
9. So the
molto
molto
F
B♭/F
F
G
great af - fair is o - ver, but who - ev - er would have guessed it would
Gm
C
B♭
F
leave us all so va - cant and so deep - ly un - im - pressed? It's

Verse 4:
He offered her on orgy in a many mirrored room
He promised her protection for the issue of her womb
She moved her body hard against a sharpened metal spoon
She stopped the bloody ritual of passage to the moon.

Verse 5:
Instrumental

Verse 6:
She took his much admired oriental frame of mind
And the heart-of-darkness alibi his money hides behind
She took his blonde madonna and his monastery wine
"This mental space is occupied and everything is mine."

Verse 7:
He tried to make a final stand beside the railway track
She said, "The art of longing's over and it's never coming back."
She took his tavern parliament, his cap, his cocky dance
She mocked his female fashions and his working-class moustache.

Dress Rehearsal Rag

Words & Music by Leonard Cohen

A♯m
Bm
Cm
3fr
touch?"
I thought you knew where all of the el - e -
C♯m
4fr
A♯m
Bm
- phants lie down,
I thought you were the crown
Cm
3fr
C♯m
4fr
A♯m
prince of all the wheels in Iv - 'ry Town.
Bm
B♭m
Just take a look at your bod - y now,

Am
A♯m
there's noth - ing much to save.
Bm
B♭m
And a bit - ter voice in the mir - ror cries, "Hey,
Am
A♯m
Prince, you need a shave."
Bm
Cm
3fr
Now if you can man - age to get your trem - bling

C♯m
A♯m
Bm
fin - gers to be - have, why don't you try un-
To Coda
Cm
C♯m
A♯m
-wrap - ping a stain - less steel ra - zor blade? That's right, it's
Bm
C♯m
Am
come to this. Yes, it's come to this,
C
B♭
D
and was - n't it a long way

G
B♭
D
down?
Ah, was-n't it a strange way
1, 2.
3.
D.S. al Coda
Coda
C♯m
4fr
Cm
3fr
shows you where to hit.
And then the
Bm
Am
cam - er-as pan the stang - in stunt man,

B♭
D
G
dress__ re - hears - al rag.
It's just the
B♭
D
G
dress re - hears - al rag.
You know this
B♭
D
G
dress__ re - hears - al rag.
It's just the
B♭
D
G
dress______ re - hears - al rag.______

Diamonds In The Mine

Words & Music by Leonard Cohen

B♭
C
rust - y cans, and the trees are burn - ing in your
G7
F
prom - ised land. And there are no let - ters in the
C
G9sus4
C
F
mail - box. And there are no grapes up - on the vine.
C
G9sus4
C
F
And there are no choc - 'lates in your box -

Verse 2:
Well, you tell me that your lover has a broken limb.
You say, I'm kind-a restless now, and it's on account of him.
Well, I saw the man in question, it was just the other night.
He was eating up a lady where the lions and Christians fight.

And there are no letters in the mailbox *etc.*

Verse 3:
Ah, there is no comfort in the covens of the witch.
Some very clever doctor went and sterilized the bitch.
And the only man of energy, yes, the revolution's pride.
He trained a hundred women just to kill an unborn child.

And there are no letters in the mailbox *etc.*

The Faith

Words & Music by Leonard Cohen

* Leonard sings 2 octaves lower.

Bm7 E E9/G♯ A
The club, the wheel, the mind; oh
Your vow, your ho - ly place; oh
Bm C♯7 F♯m A
love, aren't you tired___ yet? The club, the
love, aren't you tired___ yet? The blood, the
D E11 A Bm E7
To Coda
wheel, the mind; oh love, aren't you tired___
soil, the faith; oh love, aren't you tired___
1, 2.
A Bm A/E E7/F♯ A
yet?

Verse 3:
A cross on every hill
A star, a minaret.
So many graves to fill;
O love, aren't you tired yet?
So many graves to fill;
O love, aren't you tired yet?

Verse 4:
Instrumental

Verse 5:
The sea so deep and blind
Where still the sun must set.
And time itself unwind;
O love, aren't you tired yet?
And time itself unwind;
O love, aren't you tired yet?

The Gypsy's Wife

Words & Music by Leonard Cohen

C
D
thresh - ing floor?
Whose dark - ness deep - ens
Am
C
in her arms a lit - tle more?
And where,
G
where is my gyp - sy wife to - night?
C
G
Where,
where is my gyp - sy wife to - night?

Verse 2:
Ah, the silver knives are flashing in the tired old café.
A ghost climbs on the table in a bridal negligee.
She says, "My body is the light, my body is the way."
I raise my arm against it all and I catch the bride's bouquet.

And where, where is my Gypsy wife tonight? *etc.*

Verse 3:
Too early for the rainbow, too early for the dove.
These are the final days, this is the darkness, this is the flood.
And there is no man or woman who can be touched.
But you who come between them will be judged.

And where, where is my Gypsy wife tonight? *etc.*

Heart With No Companion

Words & Music by Leonard Cohen

G
C
G
-where.
And I sing this
-less.
You must keep it
for the captain whose
D
G
C
ship has not been built, for the moth-er in con-
G
D
G
-fus-ion, her cra-dle still un-filled. For the
C
G
D
heart with no com-pan-ion, for the soul with-out a

G
C
G
king. For the pri - ma bal - le - ri - na who can-not
D
1.
G
2.
G
D.S. al Coda
dance to an - y - thing. 2. Through the - thing. And I
Coda
G
Harmonica
C
- where.
G
D
G

Hallelujah

Words & Music by Leonard Cohen

B♭
E♭
6fr
F
Gm
E♭
6fr
seen your flag on the mar-ble arch. But lis-ten, love; love is not some kind of vic-t'ry march. No, it's a cold
F
D7
Gm
N.C.
4
and it's a ver-y bro-ken hal-le-lu-jah. Hal-le-
E♭
6fr
Gm
E♭
6fr
-lu-jah, hal-le-lu-jah, hal-le-lu-jah, hal-le-

1.
B♭
F
B♭
F
-lu, hal-le-lu-jah.
2-4.
B♭
F
B♭
F
-lu - - - - - jah.
5.
B♭
F
E♭
6fr
N.C.
Gm
-lu - jah. Hal-le - lu - jah, hal-le-lu - jah, hal-le -

Verse 2:
There was a time you let me know
What's really going on below
Ah, but now you never show it to me, do you?
Ah, but I remember, yeah, when I moved in you
And the holy dove, she was moving too
Yes, and every single breath that we drew was hallelujah.

Hallelujah, hallelujah, hallelujah, hallelujah.

Verse 3:
Maybe there's a God above
As for me, and all I ever seem to learn from love
Is how to shoot at someone who outdrew you.
Ah, but it's not a complaint that you hear tonight
It's not the laughter of someone who claims to have seen the light
No, it's a cold and it's a very lonely hallelujah.

Hallelujah, hallelujah, hallelujah, hallelujah.

Verse 4:
Instrumental

Hallelujah, hallelujah, hallelujah, hallelujah.

Verse5:
I did my best, it wasn't much
I couldn't feel, so I learned to touch
I've told the truth, I didn't come all this way to fool you.
Yeah, and even though it all went wrong
I'll stand right here before the Lord of Song
With nothing on my tongue but hallelujah.

Hallelujah, hallelujah, hallelujah, hallelujah.
Hallelujah, hallelujah, hallelujah, hallelujah.

Here It Is

Words & Music by Leonard Cohen & Sharon Robinson

D♭
E♭m
E♭m/D♭
E♭m
for all things.
(Plus Leonard: 8va bassa) 2. Here is your cart,
(Verses 4, 6 & 8 see block lyrics)
your card-board and piss;
and here is your love
for all of this.
May ev-'ry-one
A♭m7
B♭m7
live,
may ev-'ry-one die.
Hel-lo my

A♭m7
B♭7
1, 2.
love; and, my love, good - bye. (Here it is.)
3, 4.
E♭m
E♭m/D♭
(Here it is.) (Girls) 3. Here is your - bye
And may ev - 'ry - one
A♭m7
B♭m7
E♭m
live, may ev - 'ry - one die. Hel - lo my
A♭m7
B♭7
love; and, my love, good - bye. (Here it is.)

Verse 3:
Here is your wine
And your drunken fall
And here is your love
Your love for it all.

Verse 4:
Here is your sickness
Your bed and your pan
And here is your love
For the woman, the man.

May everyone live *etc.*

Verse 5:
And here is the night
The night has begun
And here is your death
In the heart of your son.

Verse 6:
And here is the dawn
Till death do us part
And here is your death
In your daughter's heart.

May everyone live *etc.*

Verse 7:
And here you are hurried
And here you are gone
And here is the love
It's all built upon.

Verse 8:
Here is your cross,
Your nails and your hill;
And here is your love,
That lists where it will

May everyone live *etc.*

Humbled In Love

Words & Music by Leonard Cohen

G G♯dim7 Am
pledged in the pas - sion - ate night? Ah, they're
C G Cm
3fr
soiled now, they're torn at the edg - es like moths on a stale yel - low
A♭7 G G♯dim7 Am
4fr
light. Now pen - ance serves to re - new them, nor
G G♯dim7 Am C
mas - sive trans - fu - sions of trust, why, not e - ven re - venge can un -

G
Cm
3fr
G
N.C.
do them, so twist - ed these vows and so crushed. And you say you've been
B♭
F
hum - bled in love, cut down in your love, forced to
B♭
F
B♭
kneel in the mud next to me. Ah, but why so bit - ter - ly
F
Am
Fmaj7
8fr
turn from the one who kneels there as deep - ly as

Verse 2:
Children have taken these pledges
They have ferried them out of the past,
Oh beyond all the graves and the hedges
Where love must go hiding at last.
And here where there is no description,
Here in the moment at hand,
No sinner need rise up forgiven,
No victim need limp to the stand.

And you say you've been humbled in love *etc.*

Verse 3:
And look dear heart, look at the virgin,
Look how she welcomes him into her gown.
Yes, and mark how the stranger's cold armour
Dissolves like a star falling down.
Why trade this vision for desire
When you may have them both.
You will never see a man this naked,
I will never hold a woman this close.

And you say you've been humbled in love *etc.*

I Can't Forget

Words & Music by Leonard Cohen

F
Dm
stum-bled out of bed, I got rea-dy for the strug-
burn - ing up the road, I'm head-ing down to
(3.) loved you all my life, and that's how I want to end
F
-gle. I smoked a cig-a-rette and I
Phoe-nix. I got this old ad-dress of
it. The sum-mer's al-most gone, the
Dm
C
B♭
B♭m
tight-ened up my gut. I said "This can't be me;
some-one that I knew. It was high and fine and
win-ter's tun-ing up. Yeah, the sum-mer's gone, but a

Gm
A
E♭
Dm
3fr
6fr
must be my dou - ble."
free, ah, you should have seen us.
lot goes on for ev - er.
F
B♭
F
And I can't for - get,
I can't for - get,
B♭
D♭
E♭
4fr
6fr
To Coda
I can't for - get, but I don't re - mem - ber
1.
2.
F
F
what.
who.
I'll be

A
Dm
A
there to - day with a big bou - quet of cac - tus. I've
E♭
6fr
Dm
C
got this rig that runs on mem - o - ries.
Dm
B♭
And I prom - ise, cross my heart, they'll nev - er
F
Dm
D♭
4fr
catch us; but if they do, just

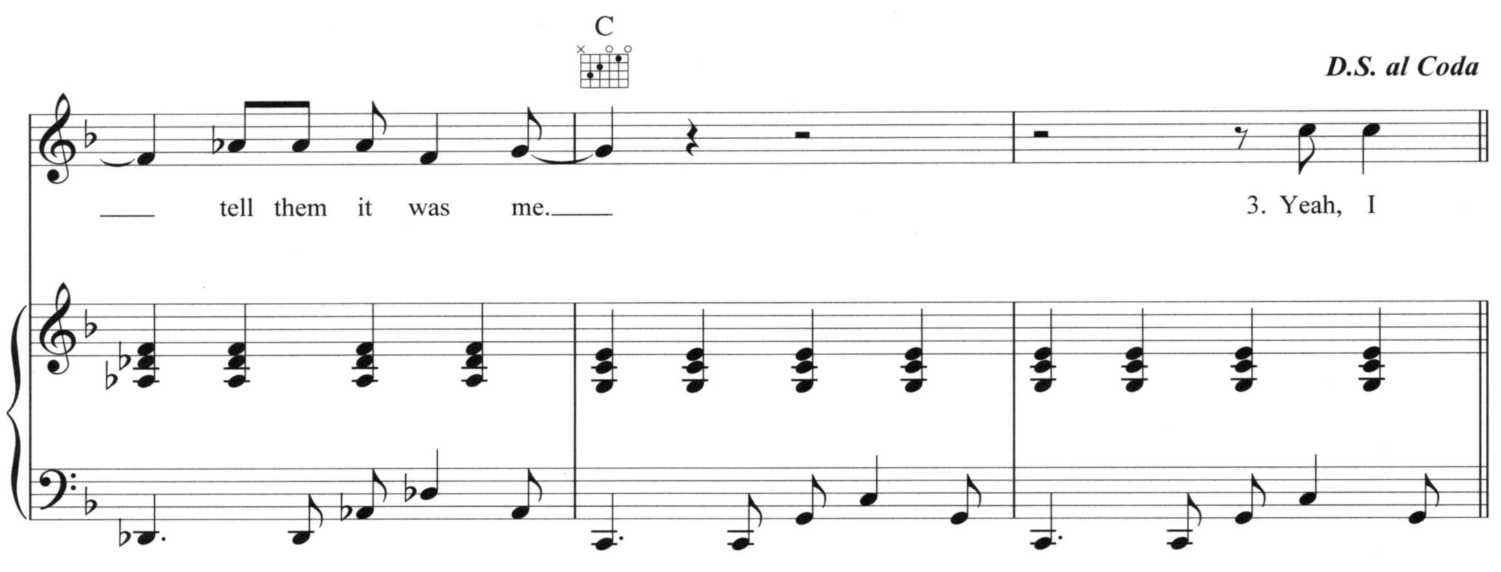
C
D.S. al Coda
tell them it was me.
3. Yeah, I

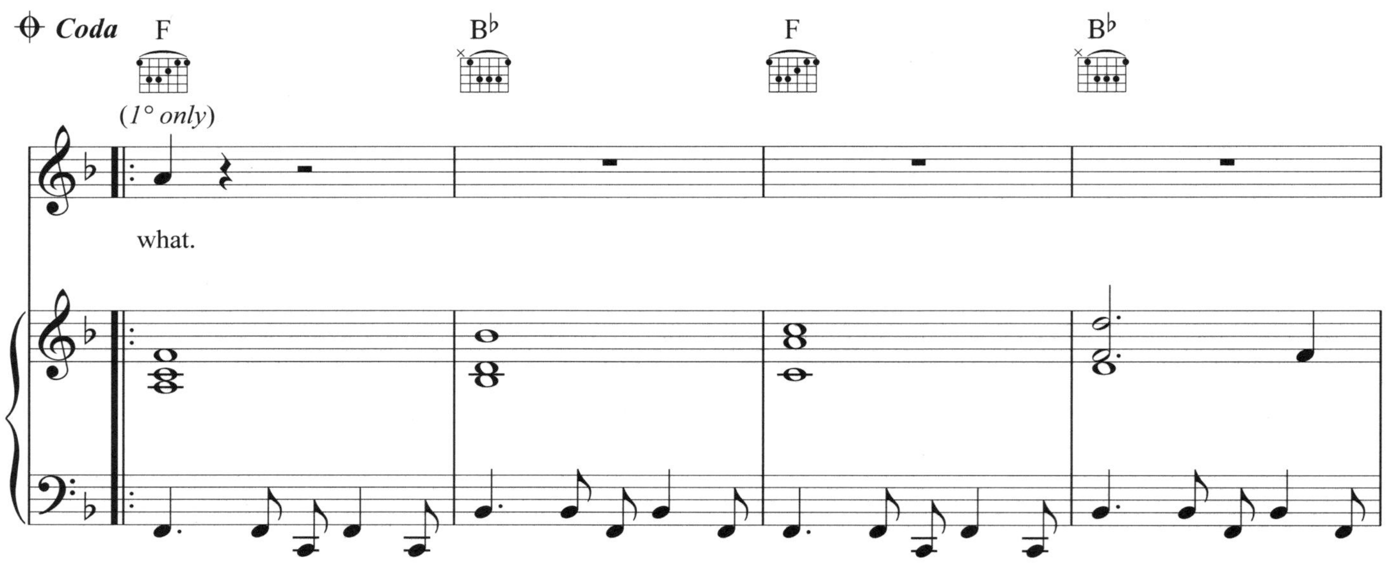
Coda
F
B♭
F
B♭
(1° only)
what.

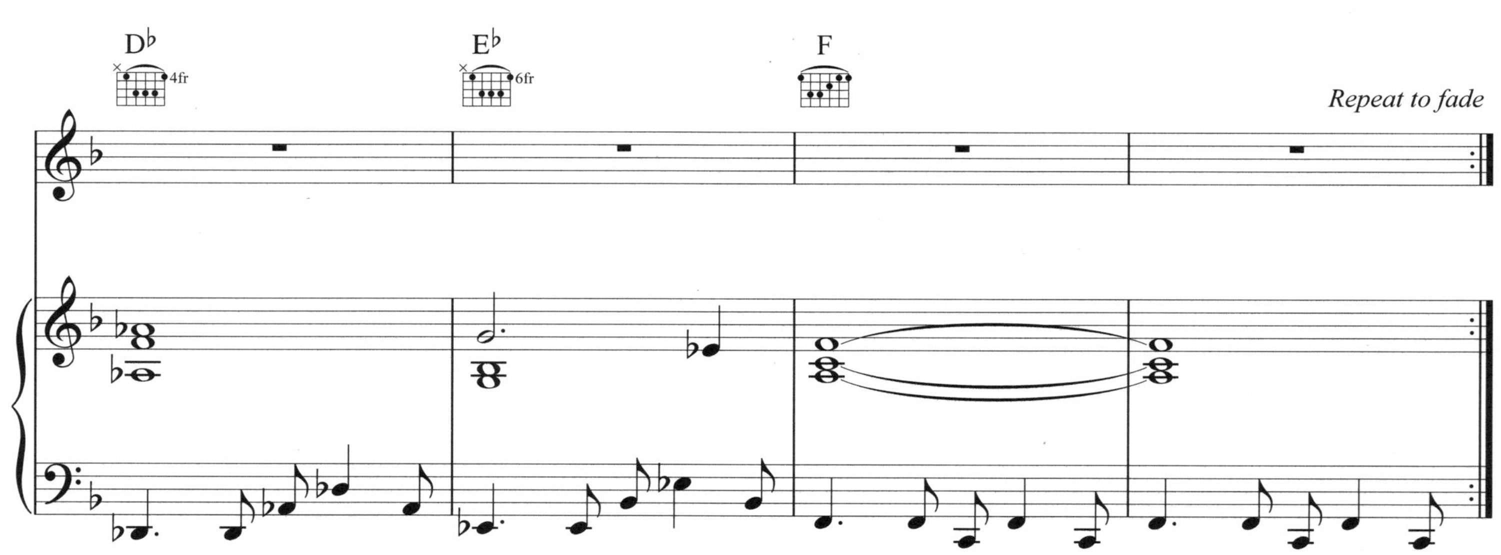
D♭
4fr
E♭
6fr
F
Repeat to fade

I Left A Woman Waiting

Words & Music by Leonard Cohen & Phil Spector

Em
A
D
Bm
you, lov - er? What hap - pened to you, my lov - er? What hap - pened to
beau - ty, hap - pened to your beau - ty. What hap - pened to your
Em
A
D
G
you, lov - er? What hap - pened to you?
beau - ty, hap - pened to me.
1.
2.
A
G
A
D
G
A
G
A
A
G
A
D
G
A
G
A
D
G
A
G
A
We took our - selves to some - one's_ bed_ and there we fell to - geth - er.

G
F♯m
Em
D
G
D
G
D/F♯
2fr
Em7
D
Quick as dogs and tru - ly dead were we.
And free as run-ning
Em
A
D
Bm
wa-ter,
free as run-ning
wa-ter,
free as run-ning
Em
A
D
Bm
wa-ter,
free as you and me.
The way_ it's got to
rit.
Em
A
N.C.
D
be,
the way__ it's got to be,
lov - er.

Is This What You Wanted

Words & Music by Leonard Cohen

G
D
I was the mon - ey lend - er.
G
You were the sen - si - tive wom - an, and
D
A7/E
D7/F♯
I was the Ver - y Rev - 'rend Freud.
G
You were the man - u - al or - ga - sm, and

D
A
N.C.
I was the dir - ty lit - tle boy. And is
Moderately slow, with a steady beat
Bm
C
this what you want - ed, to live in a house that is
Bm
A
D
haunt - ed by the ghost of you and me? Is
Bm
C
this what you want - ed, to live in a house that is

Verse 2:
You were Marlon Brando, I was Steve McQueen.
You were K.Y. Jelly, I was Vaseline.
You were The Father of Modern Medicine, I was Mr. Clean.
You where The Whore and The Beast of Babylon,
I was Rin Tin Tin.

And is this what you wanted *etc.*

Verse 3:
You got old and wrinkled, I stayed seventeen.
You lusted after so many, I lay here with one.
You defied your solitude, I came through alone.
You said you could never love me, I undid your gown.

And is this what you wanted *etc.*

I Tried To Leave You

Words & Music by Leonard Cohen

E
Bm
E
well I don't de - ny.
I closed my
you lose your pride.
The ba - by's
I hope you're sa-tis - fied.
The bed is kind of
Bm
D
A
book on us at least a hun-dred times,
I'd
cry - ing,
so you do not go out - side,
and
nar - row,
but my arms are o - pen wide,
C
G
wake up ev - 'ry morn - ing by your side.
all your work, it's right be-fore your eyes.
and here's a man still work - ing for your smile.

1, 2.
B
N.C.
3.
B
N.C.
E
N.C.
Repeat to fade

Joan Of Arc

Words & Music by Leonard Cohen

E
D
man to get her through this ver - y smok - y
A
A7
night.
D
A
She said, "I'm tired of the war,
G
Em
D
I want the kind of work I had be - fore,

E
E7
A
B7
a wed-ding dress or some - thing white to
E
D
A
D
wear up - on my swol - len ap - pe -
A
- tite."
La la la, la la la, la la la la la

Em
la.
La la la la la
G
la,
la la la la la,
D
A
A7
la la la la la
1-3.
D
la.
2. Well, I'm

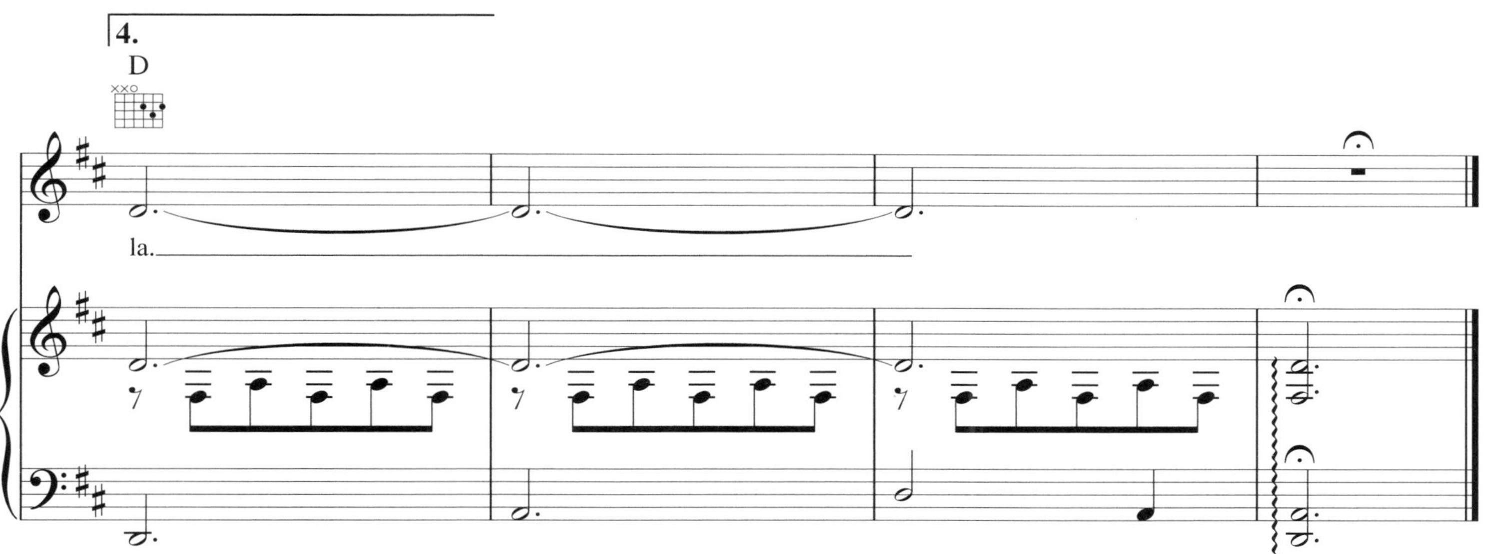

Verse 2:
Well, I'm glad to hear you talk this way,
You know I've watched you riding every day.
And something in me yearns to win
Such a cold and lonesome heroine.
"And who are you?" she sternly spoke
To the one beneath the smoke.
"Why, I'm fire," he replied
"And I love your solitude, I love your pride."

La la la la *etc.*

Verse 3:
"Then fire, make your body cold
I'm going to give you mine to hold."
Saying this she climbed inside
To be his one, to be his only bride.
And deep into his fiery heart,
He took the dust of Joan of Arc.
And high above the wedding guests
He hung the ashes of her wedding dress.

La la la la *etc.*

Verse 4:
It was deep into his fiery heart
He took the dust of Joan of Arc.
And then she clearly understood,
If he was fire, oh then she must be wood.
I saw her wince, I saw her cry,
I saw the glory in her eye.
Myself I long for love and light,
But must it come so cruel, and oh so bright!

La la la la *etc.*

Jazz Police

Words & Music by Leonard Cohen & Jeffrey Fisher

A7♯5♯11♭9
5fr
D9
4fr
Gm
3fr
N.C.
Wednes - day morn - ing can't be - lieve my ears.
I in trou - ble with the Jazz Po - lice?
Gm
3fr
E♭9
5fr
Jazz Po - lice are look - ing through my fold - ers.
Gm
3fr
E♭m
6fr
D♭m
4fr
Jazz Po - lice are talk - ing to my niece.
Gm
3fr
Gm6
3fr
To Coda
Jazz Po - lice have got their fi - nal or - ders.

A7♯5♯11
5fr
D9♭5
4fr
Gm6
3fr
N.C.
Jazz - er, drop your axe, it's Jazz Po - lice.
Am
F9
Je - sus tak - en se - ri - ous by man - y.
Am
Fm
E♭m
6fr
Je - sus tak - en joy - ous by a few.
Am
Am6
Jazz Po - lice are paid by J. Paul Get - ty.

B7♯5♯11♯♭9
7fr
E9
6fr
Am6
Jazz - ers paid by J. Paul Get - ty Two.
B♭
B♭/D
Gm7
3fr
D/F♯
Am6
Jazz Po - lice, I hear you call - ing.
B♭/F
B♭
B♭/D
E
Emaj7
Jazz Po - lice, I feel so blue.
D♭/F
D♭
D♭/A♭
Aaug
Jazz Po - lice, I think I'm fall - ing, I'm

Dmaj7
2fr
B♭aug
N.C.
D.S. al Coda
fall - ing for you.
Coda
A7♯5♯11
5fr
D9♭5
4fr
Gm6
3fr
N.C.
Jazz - er, drop your axe, it's Jazz Po - lice.
Gm
3fr
E♭9
5fr
They will nev - er un - der - stand our cul - ture. They'll
Gm
3fr
E♭m
6fr
D♭m
4fr
nev - er un - der - stand the Jazz Po - lice.

Gm
3fr
Gm6
3fr
Jazz Po - lice are work - ing for my moth - er.
A7♯5♯11♭9
5fr
N.C.
Gm6
3fr
N.C.
Blood is thick - er mar - ga - rine than grease.
Am
F9
Let me be some - bod - y I ad - mire.
Am
Fm
E♭m
6fr
Let me be that mus - cle down the street.

Am
Aaug
Stick an - oth - er tur - tle on the fire.
B♭aug
Am
N.C.
Guys like me are mad for tur - tle meat.
B♭
B♭/D
Gm7
3fr
D/F♯
Am6
Jazz Po - lice I hear you call - ing.
B♭/F
B♭
B♭/D
E
Emaj7
Jazz Po - lice I feel so blue.

D♭/F
D♭
D♭/A♭
Aaug
Jazz Po - lice, I think I'm fall - ing, I'm
Dmaj7
2fr
B♭aug
N.C.
fall - ing for you.
Gm
3fr
E♭
Jazz Po - lice are look - ing through my fold - ers.
Gm
3fr
E♭
F
Repeat to fade
Jazz Po - lice have got their fi - nal or - ders.

Lady Midnight

Words & Music by Leonard Cohen

C7
F
but she was past all con - cern. I
C
F
Em
Dm
asked her to hold me, I said, "La - dy, un -
C
F
- fold me." But she scorned me, and she told me I was
1, 2.
G
G7
C
dead, and I could nev - er re - turn. 2. Well, I

Verse 2:
Well, I argued all night like so many have before,
Saying, "Whatever you give me, I seem to need so much more."
Then she pointed at me where I kneeled on her floor.
She said, "Don't try to use me or slyly refuse me,
Just win me or lose me, it is this that the darkness is for."

Verse 3:
I cried, "Oh, Lady Midnight, I fear that you grow old,
"Stars eat your body and the wind makes you cold."
"If we cry now," she said, "it will just be ignored."
So I walked through the morning, the sweet early morning.
I could hear my lady calling, "You've won me, you've won me, my Lord."

"You've won me, you've won me, my Lord."
"Yes, you've won me, you've won me, my Lord."

Last Year's Man

Words & Music by Leonard Cohen

A♭
4fr
E♭
6fr
past the stems of thumb-tacks that still throw sha-dows on the wood. And the
a tempo ♩ = 76 accel.
A♭
4fr
F
B♭
F
sky-light is like skin for a drum I'll nev-er mend; and
(accel.)
B♭
Gm
3fr
N.C.
A♭
4fr
all the rain falls down, a-men, on the works
♩ = 112 accel.
E♭
6fr
of last year's man.

♩ = 120
B♭
2. I met a la - dy, she was play - ing with her
(Verses 3-5. see block lyrics)
Gm
3fr
sol - diers in the dark. Oh,
A♭
4fr
one by one she had to tell them that her
E♭
6fr
name was Joan of Arc.

B♭
I was in that ar - my, yes, I
Gm
stayed a lit - tle while.
A♭
4fr
I want to thank you, Joan of Arc,
E♭
6fr
for treat - ing me so well.

A♭
4fr
F
And though I wear a u - ni - form, I
B♭
F
was not born to fight. All these
1-3.
poco rit.
B♭
Gm
3fr
A♭
4fr
wound - ed boys you lie be - side, good- night my
a tempo
E♭
6fr
friends, good - night.

4.
poco accel.
Gm
rit.
A♭
3fr
4fr
down, a - men, on the works of last year's
E♭
6fr
man.
a tempo
B♭
Gm
3fr
Girls: Mm.
Mm.
A♭
4fr
Mm.

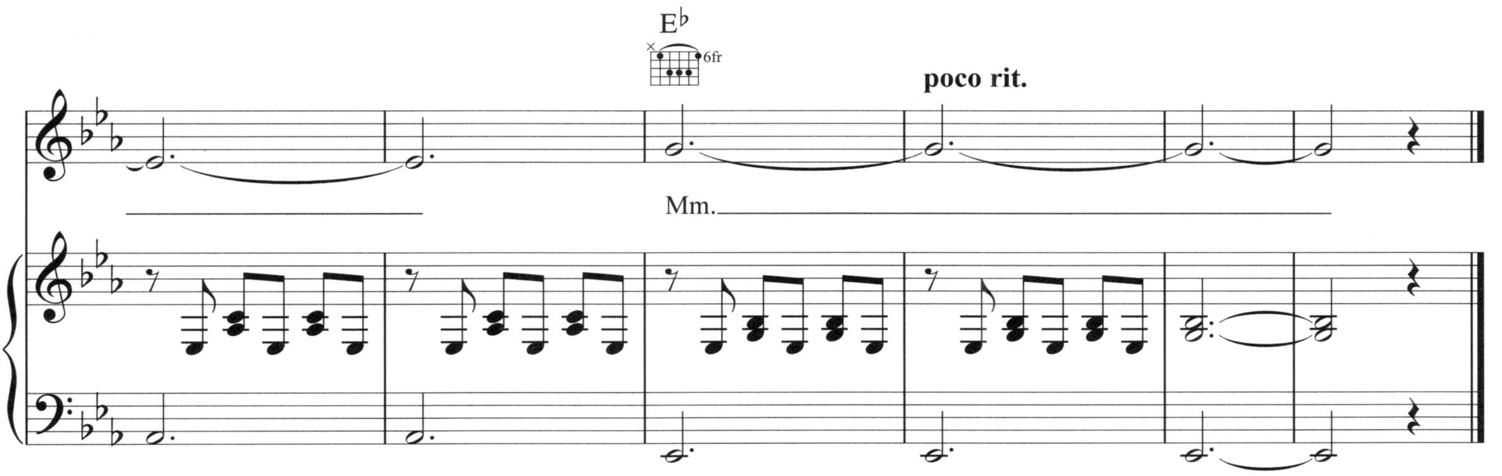

Verse 3:
I came upon a wedding
That old families had contrived,
Bethlehem the bridegroom
Babylon the bride.
Great Babylon was naked
Oh, she stood there trembling for me
And Bethlehem inflamed us both
Like the shy one at some orgy.
And when we fell together
All our flesh was like a veil
That I had to draw aside to see
The serpent eat its tail.

Verse 4:
Some women wait for Jesus
And some women wait for Cain,
So I hang upon my altar
And I hoist my axe again.
And I take the one who finds me
Back to where it all began,
When Jesus was the honeymoon
And Cain was just the man.
And we read from pleasant Bibles
That are bound in blood and skin,
That the wilderness is gathering
All its children back again.

Verse 5:
The rain falls down
On last year's man
An hour has gone by
And he has not moved his hand.
But everything will happen
If he only gives the word,
The lovers will rise up
And the mountains touch the ground.
But the skylight is like skin
For a drum I'll never mend
And all the rain falls down, amen,
On the works of last year's man.

The Land Of Plenty

Words & Music by Leonard Cohen & Sharon Robinson

A♭ B♭m/F G♭ A♭ B♭m/F G♭
4fr 4fr
real - ly have the temp-'ra - ment to lend a help-ing hand. Don't
what you real - ly think of me, what I real - ly think of you. For the
I can't buy it, ba - by, I can't buy it an - y - more. And I don't
D♭maj7 Cm7 Fm B♭m9 E♭7
4fr 3fr 3fr 6fr
real - ly know who sent me to raise my voice and say "May the
mil - lions in a pri - son that wealth has set a - part, for the
real - ly know who sent me to raise my voice and say "May the
A♭ G♭ D♭maj7 E♭7
4fr 4fr 6fr
lights in the land of plen - ty shine on the truth some -
Christ who has not ris - en from the ca - verns of the
lights in the land of plen - ty shine on the truth some -

1.
A♭
B♭m/F
G♭
4fr
- day." 2. I
2, 3.
heart.
- day".
For the
For the
Fm
E♭/G
A♭
3fr
in - ner-most de - ci - sion that we
can - not but o - bey, for what's left of our re - li - gion,
D♭
E♭
6fr
To Coda

B♭
E♭
6fr
D♭/E♭
6fr
E♭
6fr
I lift my voice and pray "May the
A♭
4fr
B♭m/F
G♭
A♭
4fr
B♭m/F
G♭
lights in the land of plen-ty, may the
A♭
4fr
B♭m/F
G♭
A♭
4fr
B♭m/F
G♭
lights in the land of plen-ty, may the

A♭ G♭ D♭maj7 E♭7
lights in the land of plen-ty, shine on the truth some
A♭ B♭m/F G♭ A♭ B♭m/F G♭
D.S. (2°) al Coda
day. 3. I
Coda B♭sus4 B♭ E♭sus4 E♭
lift my voice and pray "May the
A♭ B♭m/F G♭ A♭ B♭m/F G♭
lights in the land of plen-ty, may the

A♭
B♭m/F
G♭
4fr
lights in the land of plen - ty,
may the
A♭
G♭
D♭maj7
E♭7
6fr
lights in the land of plen - ty,
shine on the truth some -
- day."
Repeat to fade

The Law

Words & Music by Leonard Cohen

F
Dm
Dsus2/4
Dm
but I do un - der - stand,
there's a law,
B♭
A7
Dm
there's an arm,
there's a hand.
There'a a law,
B♭
A7
1, 2, 4.
Dm
A7(OMIT3)
there's an arm,
there's a hand.
3.
Dm
5.
Dm
2. Now my heart's like a
There's a law,

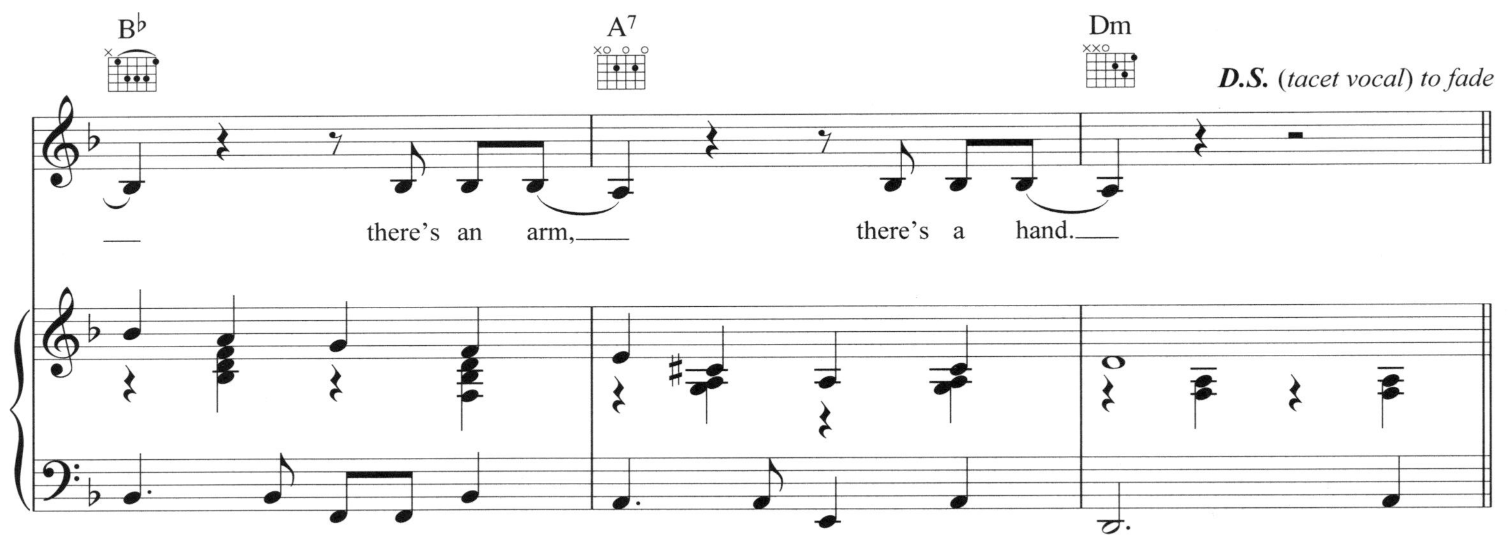

Verse 2:
Now my heart's like a blister
From doing what I do,
If the moon has a sister
It's got to be you.
I'm gonna miss you forever
Though it's not what I planned.
There's a law, there's an arm, there's a hand.
There's a law, there's an arm, there's a hand.

Verse 3:
Now the deal has been dirty
Since dirty began,
I'm not asking for mercy,
Not from the man.
You just don't ask for mercy
While you're still on the stand.
There's a law, there's an arm, there's a hand.
There's a law, there's an arm, there's a hand.

Verse 4:
Instrumental
I don't claim to be guilty,
Guilty's too grand.
There's a law, there's an arm, there's a hand.
There's a law, there's an arm, there's a hand.

Verse 5:
That's all I can say, baby
That's all I can say,
It wasn't for nothing
That they put me away.
I fell with my angel
Down the chain of command.
There's a law, there's an arm, there's a hand.
There's a law, there's an arm, there's a hand.
There's a law, there's an arm, there's a hand.

Light As The Breeze

Words & Music by Leonard Cohen

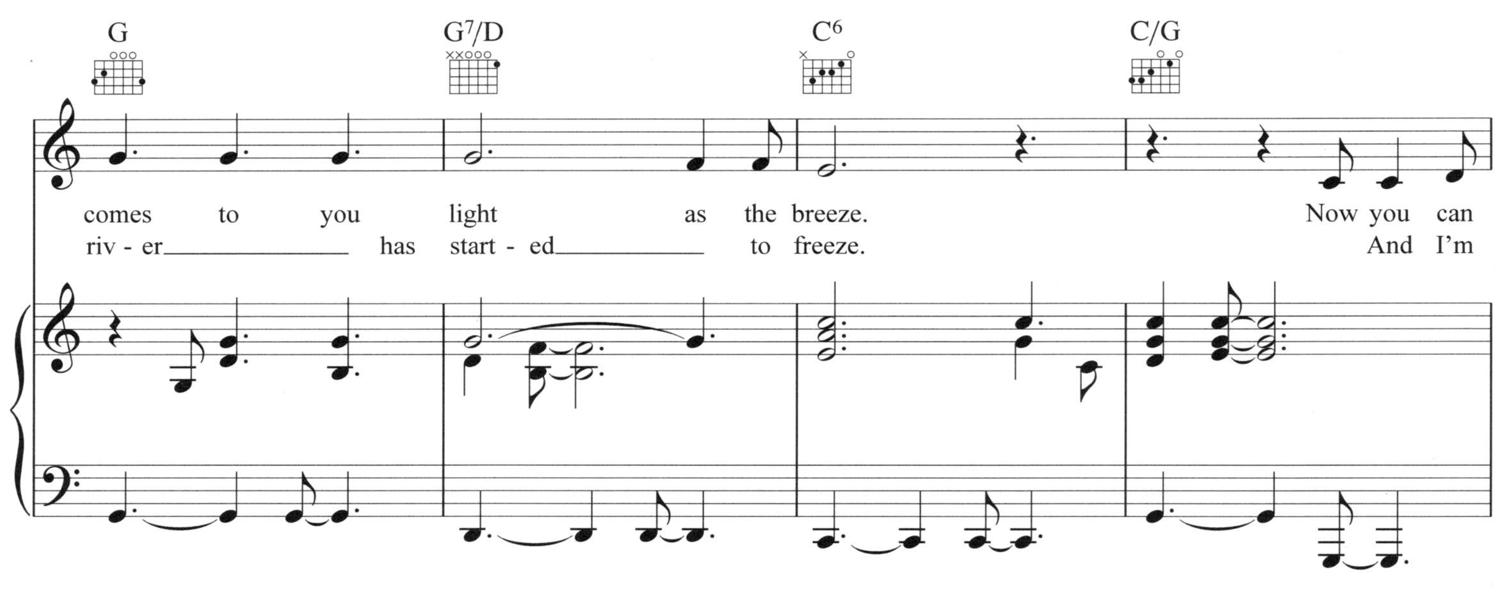
G G7/D C6 C/G
comes to you light as the breeze. Now you can
riv - er has start - ed to freeze. And I'm

C C6/G Dm Dm/A
drink it or you can nurse it, it don't mat - ter how you wor - ship, as
sick of pre - tend - ing, I'm bro - ken from bend - ing. I've

G G13/D C6 C/G
3fr
long as you're down on your knees. 2. So I
lived too long on my knees. 5. And she

C
C6/G
Dm
knelt there at the del - ta, at the al - pha and the o -
(3.) weak and you're harm - less and you're sleep - ing in your
(5.) dan - ces so grace - ful, and your heart's hard and
(6.) blood on ev - 'ry brace - let, you can see it, you can
Dm/A
G
G7/D
-me - ga, at the cra - dle of the riv - er and the
har - ness, and the wind go - ing wild in the
hate - ful; and she's nak - ed, but that's just a
taste it; and it's "Please ba - by, please ba - by, please."
C6
C/G
C
C6/G
seas. And, like a bless - ing come from heav - en, for
trees. And it ain't ex - act - ly pri - son, but you'll
tease. And you turn in dis - gust from your
And she says "Drink deep - ly, pil - grim, but don't for-

Dm
Dm/A
G
some - thing like a se - cond I was healed and my heart
nev - er be for - giv - en forwhat - ev - er you've
ha - tred and from your love, andshe comes to you
- get there's still a wom - an be - neath this re -
G13/D
3fr
C6
C/G
was at ease.
done with the keys.
light as a breeze.
- splend - ent che - mise." (4° spoken, freely)
Ah
So I
E
E7/B
Asus4
Am/E
ba - by, I wait - ed so long for your kiss, for
knelt there at the delta, at the alpha and the o - mega; I

E
E7/B
F6
6fr
F/C
some - thing to hap - pen, ah, some - thing like
knelt there like one who believes. And the
C
C6/G
A♭dim
this. 3° only (Some - thing like this.)
blessings come from heaven; and, for something like a
Ddim
Gsus4
G7sus4/D
second, I'm cured and my heart is at
1, 3.
2, 4.
2° D.S.
4° D.S. Instrumental to fade
G7
G7/D
G7
G7/D
G7
ease.
3. And you're
6. There's
4. It's

Love Calls You By Your Name

Words & Music by Leonard Cohen

B♭
G
Em
the beast so ver - y tame. But here, right
Am
G
here, between the birth - mark and the stain, be-tween the
Am
G
Am
o - cean and your o - pen vein, be-tween the snow - man and the
G
F
D
F
rain, once a - gain, once a - gain, love

Verse 2:
The women in your scrapbook
Whom you still praise and blame,
You say they chained you to your fingernails,
And you climb the halls of fame.
But here, right here,
Between the peanuts and the cage,
Between the darkness and the stage,
Between the hour and the age,
Once again, once again,
Love calls you by your name.

Verse 3:
Shouldering your loneliness
Like a gun that you will not learn to aim,
You stumble into this movie house,
Then you climb, you climb into the frame.
Yes, and here, right here,
Between the moonlight and the lane,
Between the tunnel and the train,
Between the victim and his stain,
Once again, once again,
Love calls you by your name.

Verse 4:
I leave the lady meditating
On the very love which I, I do not wish to claim.
I journey down the hundred steps,
But the street is still the very same.
And here, right here,
Between the dancer and his cane,
Between the sailboat and the drain,
Between the newsreel and your tiny pain,
Once again, once again,
Love calls you by your name.

Verse 5:
Where are you, Judy? Where are you, Anne?
Where are the paths your heroes came?
Wondering out loud as the bandage pulls away,
Was I, was I only limping, was I really lame?
Oh here, come over here,
Between the windmill and the grain,
Between the sundial and the chain,
Between the traitor and her pain,
Once again, once again,
Love calls you by your name.

Lover Lover Lover

Words & Music by Leonard Cohen

Am
us - ing now is cov - ered up with fear and filth and cow - ard - ice and
Em
D
Em
D
Em
D
Em
shame."
Yes, and
C
lov - er, lov - er, lov - er, lov - er, lov - er, lov - er, lov - er, come
G
back to me.
Yes, and

Verse 2:
He said, "I locked you in this body, I meant it as a kind of trial.
You can use it for a weapon, or to make some woman smile."

Yes and lover, lover, lover, *etc.*

Verse 3:
"Then let me start again," I cried, "Please let me start again.
I want a face that's fair this time, I want a spirit that is calm."

Yes and lover, lover, lover, *etc.*

Verse 4:
"I never turned aside," he said, "I never walked away.
It was you who built the temple, it was you who covered up my face."

Yes and lover, lover, lover, *etc.*

Verse 5:
And may the spirit of this song, may it rise up pure and free.
May it be a shield for you, a shield against the enemy.

Yes and lover, lover, lover, *etc. to fade*

The Letters

Words & Music by Leonard Cohen & Sharon Robinson

E♭
6fr
D
Gm
3fr
let-ters meant.
2. You're read-ing them a-gain,
D7
Gm
3fr
D7
the ones you did-n't burn,
you
Gm
3fr
D7
E♭
6fr
press them to your lips,
my pa-ges of con - cern.
D
Cm
3fr
D7
Gm
3fr
(+ Girl) 3. I said there'd been a flood,

Cm
D7
Gm
Fsus4
I said there's noth-ing left.
I hoped that you would come,
E♭
Dsus4
D
I gave you my ad-dress.
(Girl 8vb) 4. You're
G♯m
D♯7
G♯m
sto-ry was so long,
the plot was so in - tense,
5. The wound-ed forms ap-pear,
the loss, the full ex-tent,
D♯7
G♯m
D♯7
it took you years to cross
the lines of
and sim-ple kind - ness here,
the sol-i-

1.
2.
E
7fr
D♯
6fr
E
7fr
D♯
6fr
self de - fence.
- tude of strength.
E
7fr
D♯7
6fr
G♯m
4fr
C♯m
4fr
D♯7
6fr
(Both) 6. I said there'd been a flood,
I said there's noth - ing left.
G♯m
4fr
F♯sus4
E
7fr
I hoped that you would come,
D♯sus4
6fr
D♯
6fr
I gave you my ad - dress.
7. You

Gm
3fr
D7
Gm
3fr
walk in - to my room,
you stand there at my desk,
D7
Gm
3fr
D7
be - gin your let-ter to
the one who's
Gm
3fr
D7
E♭
6fr
com- ing next.
(Girl 8vb) Be - gin your let-ter to
D
E♭
6fr
D
ooh
the one who's com-ing
(Leonard, spoken) You

Gm
3fr
D7
Gm
3fr
D7
(1° only)
next.
never liked to get the letters that I sent, but now you've got the gist of what my letters meant.
I said there'd been a flood; I said there's nothing left. I hoped that you would come, I gave you my address.
Gm
3fr
D7
E♭
6fr
You're reading them again, the ones you didn't burn, you press them to your lips,
Your story was so long, the plot was so intense, it took you years to cross
1.
D
2.
D
Gm
3fr
my pages of concern.
the lines of self-defence.
The wounded forms appear,
D7sus4
Gm
3fr
N.C.
the loss, the full extent, and simple kindness here, the solitude of strength.

Master Song

Words & Music by Leonard Cohen

B♭
Am
-pose that he told you ev - 'ry - thing that I
B♭
Am
keep locked a - way in my head. Your
B♭
Dm
mas - ter took you trav - el - ling, well, at
F
G
To Coda
least that's what you said. And

C
Em
C
Em
now do you come back to bring your
F
pris - on - er
wine and
1-7.
E
8.
E
D.C. al Coda
bread?
do.
Coda
G
C
Em
F
I come back to bring your pris - on - er

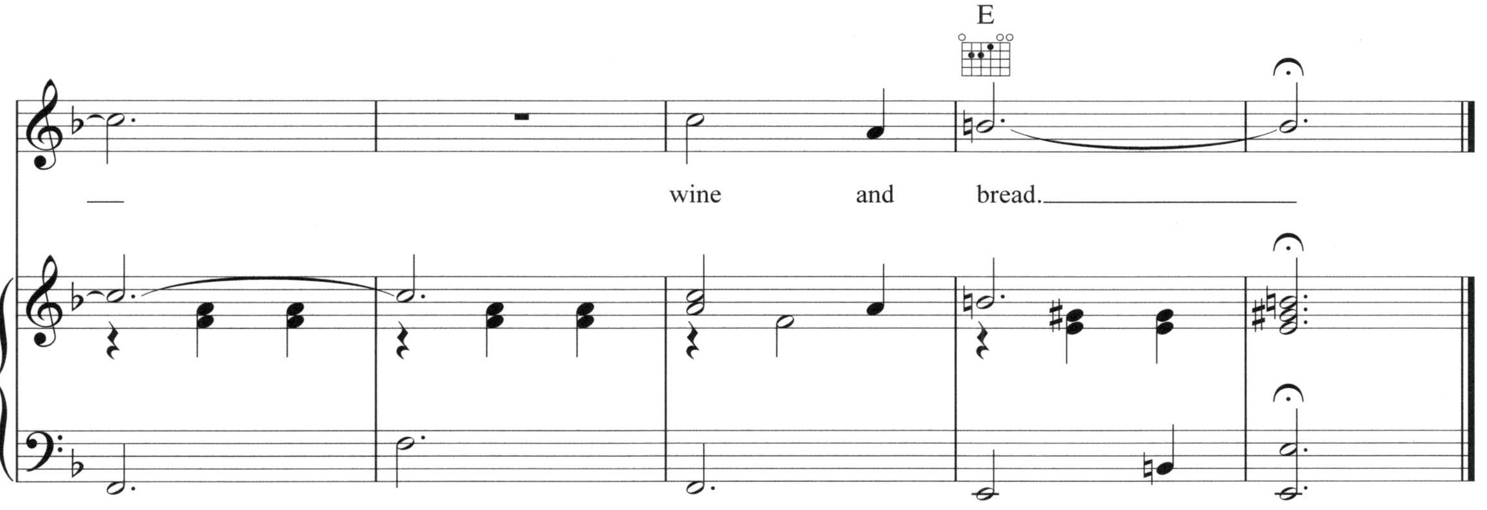

Verse 2:
You met him at some temple,
Where take your clothes at the door.
He was just a numberless man in a chair
Who'd just come back from the war.
And you wrap up his tired face in your hair,
And he hands you the apple core.
Then he touches your lips, now so suddenly bare
Of all the kisses we put on some time before.

Verse 3:
And he gave you a German Shepherd to walk
With a collar of leather and nails.
And he never once made you explain or talk
About all of the little details,
Such as who had a word and who had a rock,
And who had you through the mails.
Now your love is a secret all over the block,
And it never stops, not even when your master fails.

Verse 4:
He took you up in his aeroplane
Which he flew without any hands.
And you cruised above the ribbons of rain
That drove the crowd from the stands.
Then he killed the lights in a lonely lane
Where an ape with angel glands,
Erased the final wisps of pain
With the music of rubber bands.

Verse 5:
And now I hear your master sing,
You kneel for him to come.
His body is a golden string
That your body is hanging from.
His body is a golden string,
My body has grown numb.
Oh now you hear your master sing,
Your shirt is all undone.

Verse 6:
And will you kneel beside this bed
That we polished so long ago,
Before your master chose instead
To make my bed of snow?
Your eyes are wild and your knuckles are red,
And you're speaking far too low.
I can't make out what your master said
Before he made you go.

Verse 7:
And then I think you're playing far too rough
For a lady who's been to the moon.
I've lain by this window long enough,
To get used to an empty room.
And your love is some dust in an old man's cuff
Who is tapping his foot to a tune.
And your thighs are a ruin, and you want too much,
Let's say you came back some time too soon.

Verse 8
I loved your master perfectly,
I taught him all that he knew.
He was starving in some deep mystery
Like a man who is sure what is true.
And I sent you to him with my guarantee,
I could teach him something new.
And I taught him how you would long for me,
No matter what he said, no matter what you do.

Verse 9:
I believe that you heard your master sing
While I was sick in bed.
I'm sure that he told you everything
I must keep locked away in my head.
Your master took you travelling,
Well, at least that's what you said.
I come back to bring
Your prisoner wine and bread.

Memories

Words & Music by Leonard Cohen & Phil Spector

D
Bm
G
A
(1.) I pinned an i - ron cross_ to my la - pel. I
(3.) Chanc - es are_____ I'll let you do most_____ an - y - thing.
(4.) Bal - loons and pa - per stream ers,_____ they're float - ing down on us._____ She
D
F♯7
4fr
Bm
walked up_____ to the tall - est_____ and the blond - est girl,_
I know you're hun - gry,_____ I can hear it_ in your voice, and
says "You've got a min - ute left_____ to fall in love.". In
D
F♯7
4fr
Bm
4
I said "Look,_ you don't know me now, but ver - y_____ soon you_ will. So
there are man - y parts of me to touch,_ you have your choice. "Ah, but
sol - emn mo - ments such as this, I have put my_____ trust. And

G
D
G
D
won't you let me see, I said won't you let me see, I said
no, you can-not see." She said "No, you can-not see." She said
all my faith to see; I said all my faith to see; I said,
G
won't you let me see
"No, you can-not see.
all my faith to see
To Coda
1.
D
Bm
G
A
your na-ked bod-y?
my na-ked
her na-ked
D
Bm
G
A
2.
D
Bm
bod-y.

G
A
D
Bm
G
A
3.
D
Bm
G
A
D
Bm
(Solo continues)
G
A
D.S. al Coda
Coda
D
Bm
bod- y.
G
A
D
Bm
G
A
Repeat to fade
ad lib. vocal to fade

On That Day

Words & Music by Leonard Cohen & Anjani Thomas

G
G9/B
C
A/C♯
To Coda
I wouldn't know, I'm just holding the fort since that
I wouldn't know, I'm just holding the fort
G/D
C/D
G
D11
day they wounded New York.
G
G/B
C
G/D
Instrumental (Jaws Harp)
C6/D
2fr
G
Bm7♭5
C
C/D
D.S. al Coda

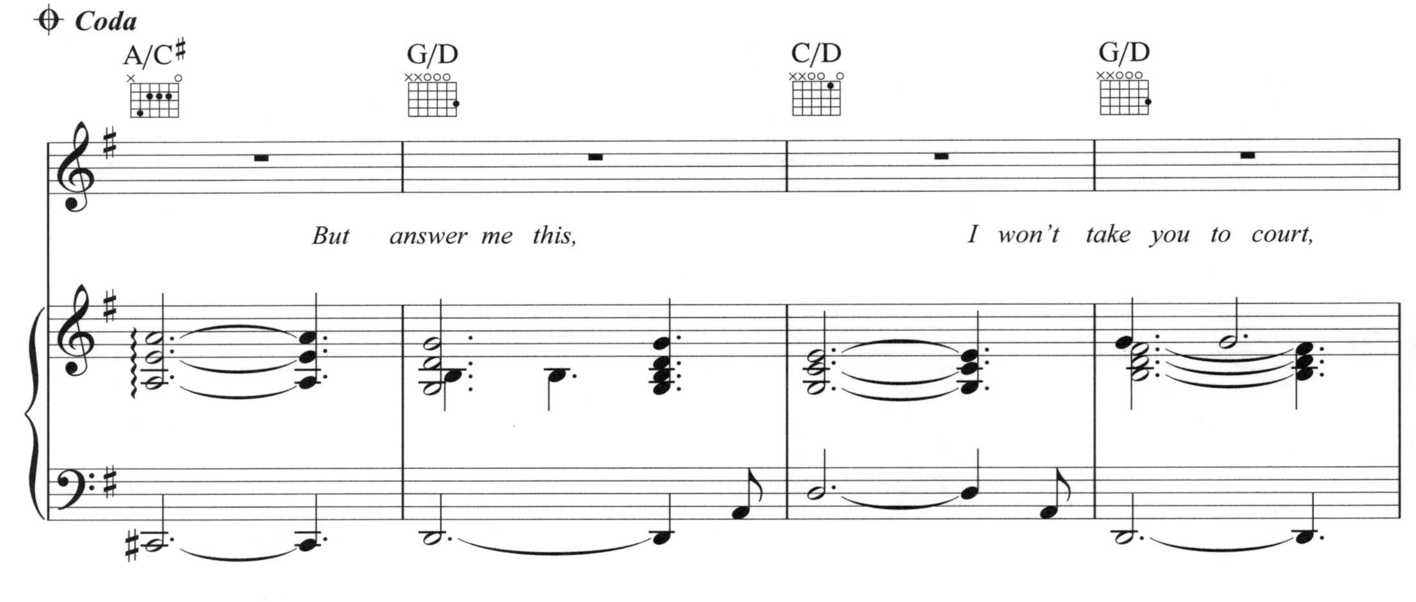
Coda
A/C♯
G/D
C/D
G/D
But answer me this,
I won't take you to court,

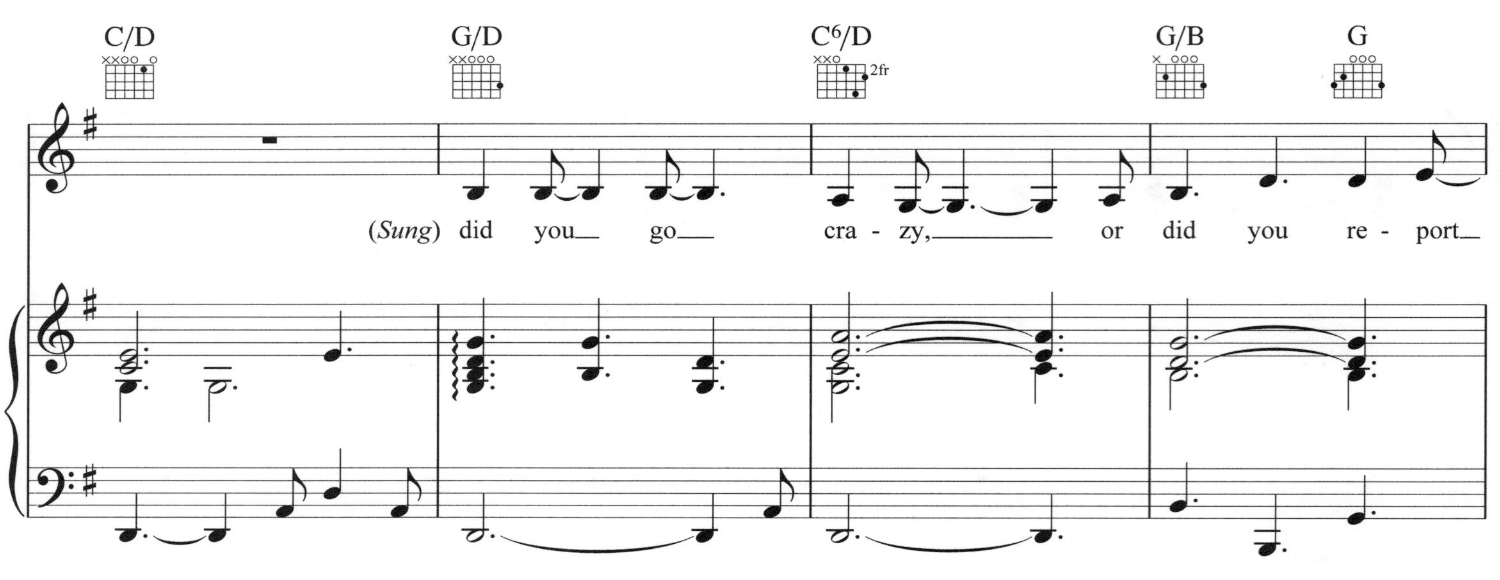
C/D
G/D
C6/D
2fr
G/B
G
(Sung) did you go crazy,
or did you report

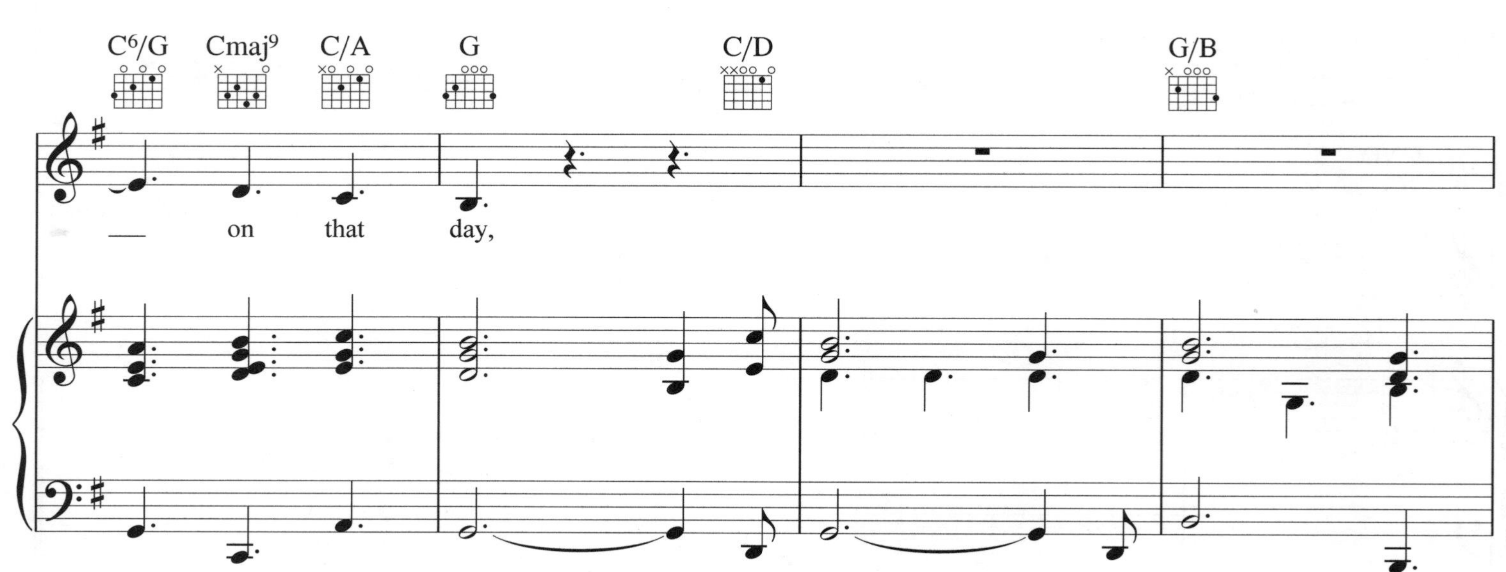
C6/G
Cmaj9
C/A
G
C/D
G/B
on that day,

C6
G/D
C6/D
2fr
G
on that day they wound - ed New York.
C/D
G
Am
G
G/B
(On
C6
G/D
C/D
G
that day they wound - ed New York.)
D5/A
2fr
G/B
Am/C
C/D
G
(Mm.)

One Of Us Cannot Be Wrong

Words & Music by Leonard Cohen

Dm
room just filled up with mos - qui - toes, they
F
G
heard that my bod - y was free. Then I
Am
Em
took the dust of a long sleep - less night, and I
F
C
put it in my lit - tle shoes. And

Verse 2:
I showed my heart to the doctor,
He said I'd just have to quit.
Then he wrote himself a prescription,
And your name was mentioned in it.
Then he locked himself in a library shelf
With the details of our honeymoon.
And I hear from the nurse
That he's gotten much worse,
And his practice is all in a ruin.

Verse 3:
I heard of a saint who had loved you,
I studied all night in his school.
He taught that the duty of lovers
Is to tarnish the golden rule.
And just when I was sure
That his teachings were pure,
He drowned himself in the pool.
His body is gone, but back here on the lawn,
His spirit continues to drool.

Verse 4:
An Eskimo showed me a movie
He'd recently taken of you.
The poor man could hardly stop shivering,
His lips and his fingers were blue.
I suppose that he froze
When the wind took your clothes,
And I guess he just never got warm
But you stand there so nice in your blizzard of ice,
Oh please let me come into the storm.

Our Lady Of Solitude

Words & Music by Leonard Cohen

A
C#m
4fr
F#m
C#m
4fr
cool.
part.
And the light came from her bod-y, and the night
F#m
C#m
4fr
went through her grace.
D
A
To Coda
E
D
All sum-mer long she touched me and I knew her, I
C#m
4fr
Bm
A
C#m
4fr
F#m
knew her face to face. And her dress was blue and

C♯m
F♯m
C♯m
4fr
sil - ver, and her words were few and small.
D
A
E
D
C♯m
Bm
She is the ves - sel of the whole wide world, mis - tress, oh, mis -
E
A
D
A
E
D.S. al Coda
- tress of us all.
2. Dear la -
rit.
Coda
E
D
C♯m
E9
A
knew her, I knew her face to face.

Paper-Thin Hotel

Words & Music by Leonard Cohen & Phil Spector

Gm
3fr
C
Am
A♭aug
C/G
F♯m7♭5
love to him. The strug-gle mouth to mouth and limb to limb,
clear be-fore. You ran your bath and you be-gan to sing;
Dm
D♭aug
2fr
F/C
Bm7♭5
G9
the grunt of u-ni-ty when he came in.
I felt so good I could-n't feel a thing.
8va
Fmaj7
Gm/F
Gm7/F
2,4. I stopped there with my ear a-gainst the wall,
5. You are the na-ked an-gel in my heart,
Fmaj7
Gm/F
Gm7/F
I was not seized by jeal-ous-y at all.
you are the wom-an with her legs a-part.

F
Gm
3fr
Gm7
3fr
In fact, a bur - den lift - ed from my soul,
It's writ-ten on the walls of this ho - tel,
To Coda ⊕
C
F
F6
Fmaj7
F6
I heard that love was out of my con-trol.
A heav-y bur-den lift-ed
"You go to Heav-en once you've been to Hell".
Gm
3fr
Gm7
3fr
C
F
F6
from my soul,
I heard that love was out of my con-trol.
1.
2.
Fmaj7
F6
Gm
3fr
C
Gm7
3fr
C
Gm7
3fr
C

F
F♯dim
Gm
3fr
C7
And I can't wait to tell you to your face,
F
F♯dim
Gm
3fr
C
D.S. al Coda
and I can't wait for you to take my place.
Coda
Fmaj7
F6
Gm
3fr
C
F
A heav-y bur-den lift-ed
rit.
Gm
3fr
Gm7
3fr
C
F
from my soul, I heard that love was out of my con-trol.

Seems So Long Ago, Nancy

Words & Music by Leonard Cohen

A
C♯
4fr
F♯m
stone. In the House of Hon - es - ty
D
A
her fa - ther was on tri - al.
E
F♯m
C♯
4fr
In the House of Mys - ter - y, there was no
D
A
E
one at all, there was no one at

Verse 2:
It seems so long ago,
None of us were strong.
Nancy wore green stockings,
And she slept with everyone.
She never said she'd wait for us,
Although she was alone.
I think she fell in love for us
In nineteen sixty-one,
In nineteen sixty-one.

Verse 3:
It seems so long ago,
Nancy was alone.
A forty-five beside her head,
An open telephone.
We told her she was beautiful,
We told her she was free.
But none of us would meet her in
The House of Mystery,
The House of Mystery.

Verse 4:
And now you look around you,
See her everywhere.
Many use her body,
Many comb her hair.
In the hollow of the night,
When you are cold and numb,
You hear her talking freely then,
She's happy that you've come,
She's happy that you've come.

Sing Another Song, Boys

Words & Music by Leonard Cohen

Cm
3fr
The mon-ey len-der's love-ly lit-tle daugh-ter, ah,
(See additional lyrics)
B♭
F9sus4
B♭
she's eat-en, she's eat-en with de-sire.
Dm
Gm
3fr
She spies him through the glass-es, from the
Dm
E♭
6fr
B♭
pawn-shops of her wick-ed fath-er.

Dm
Gm
3fr
She hails him with a mi - cro - phone that some poor
Dm
E♭
6fr
B♭
sin - ger just like me had to leave her.
Cm
3fr
B♭
F/A
She tempts him with a cla - ri - net.
Gm
3fr
F
She waves a Na - zi dag - ger.

B♭
F
B♭
F9sus4
B♭
2. She finds him ly - ing in a heap.
(Verse 3 see block lyrics)
F
B♭
F9sus4
B♭
She wants to be his wom - an.
1.
E♭
6fr
B♭9sus4
E♭
6fr
He says, "Yes, I just might go to sleep. But kind - ly
B♭
F9sus4
B♭
F9sus4
B♭
leave, leave the fu - ture, leave it o - pen."

2.
Cm
3fr
It's float-ing bro-ken on the o-pen sea, look at them, my friends,
B♭
F9sus4
B♭
and it car-ries no sur-vi-vors.
Dm
Gm
3fr
But let's leave these lov-ers won-d'ring
Dm
E♭
6fr
B♭
why they can-not have each oth-er.

Dm
Gm
3fr
And let's sing anoth-er song, boys.
Dm
E♭
6fr
B♭
This one has grown old and bit-ter.
Cm
3fr
La la la, la la la, la la la la la la la la
B♭
Cm
3fr
la la, la la la la la la la la, la la la la

Additional lyrics: (after 1st ending)
He stands where it is steep,
Ah, I guess he thinks that he's the very first one.
His hands upon his leather belt now,
Like it was the wheel of some big ocean liner.
And she will learn to touch herself so well,
As all the sails burn down like paper,
And he has with the chain of his famous cigarillo.

Verse 3:
They'll never, they'll never ever reach the moon,
At least not the one that we're after.
(*To 2nd ending*)

A Singer Must Die

Words & Music by Leonard Cohen

F
D7sus2
crimes that are mine. I will ask for the mer - cy that you
G
C
love to de - cline. And all the la - dies go moist, and the
E7sus4/B
E7/B
Am
judge has no choice. A sing - er must die for the
1, 2, 3.
4.
G
poco rit.
lie in his voice. 2. And I get - ting home late. La la

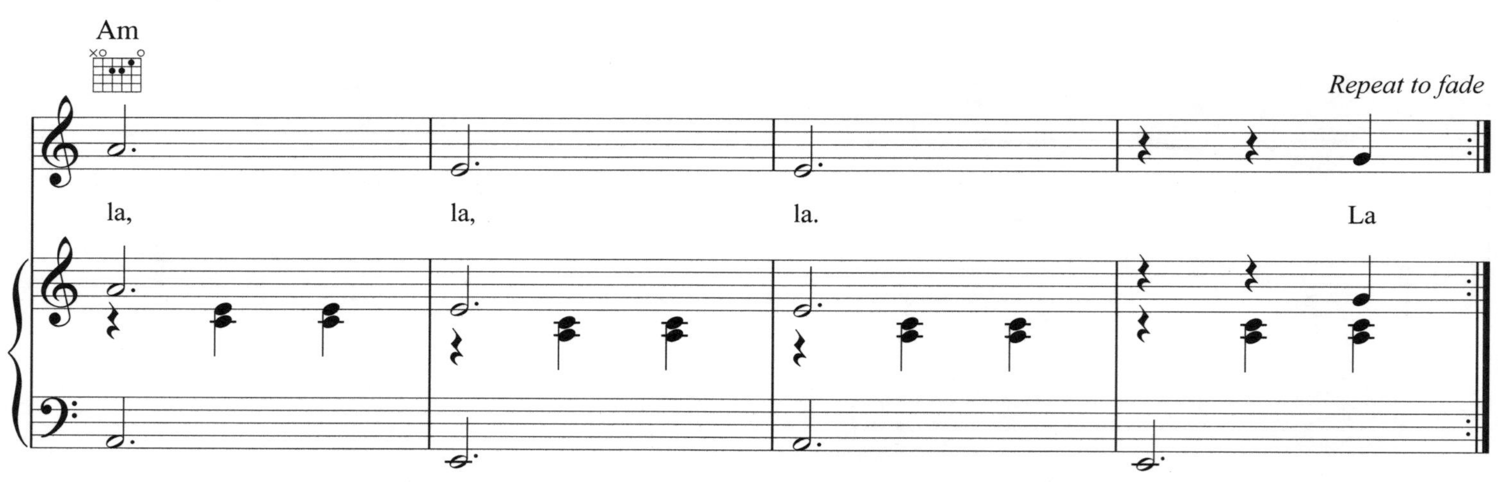

Verse 2:
And I thank you, I thank you for doing your duty,
You keepers of Truth, you guardians of Beauty.
Your vision is right, my vision is wrong,
I'm sorry for smudging the air with my song.
La la la la, la la la la la la,
La la la la la, la la la la la la.

Verse 3:
The night, it is thick, my defences are hid
In the clothes of a woman I would like to forgive,
In the rings of her silk, in the hinge of her thighs,
Where I have to go begging in beauty's disguise.
Goodnight, goodnight, my night after night,
My night after night, after night, after night.

Verse 4:
I am so afraid that I listen to you
Your sun glassed protectors they do that to you.
It's their ways to detain, their ways to disgrace,
Their knee in your balls and their fist in your face.
Yes, and long live the state, by whoever it's made.
Sir, I didn't see nothing, I was just getting home late.

The Smokey Life

Words & Music by Leonard Cohen

C
E7♯9
C
C/B♭
F/A
A♭7
4fr
where long a - go we a - greed to keep it light, so
C
C/B♭
F/A
A♭7
4fr
C7/G
F
Fm
let's be mar - ried one more night. It's light, light e -
Cm
3fr
E7♭9
C7♭9
8fr
E7♯9
C
E7♭9
C7/G
-nough to let it go. It's
F
Fm
C
E7♯9
C
B♭/D
Cm/E♭
light e - nough to let it go.

E7
Am
D
Re-mem-ber when the scen-er-y start-ed fad-ing,
Am
D
E7
I held you till you learned to walk on
Am
D
Am
D
C/E
F
air.
So don't look down,
G/F
Em7
Am7
the ground is gone, there's no-one wav-ing an-y-way, the

D
Dm7
G7
1.
smok - ey life is prac - ticed ev - 'ry - where.
2.
C
C/B♭
F/A
A♭7
4fr
Come on back if the mo - ment lends, you can
C
C/B♭
F/A
A♭7
4fr
C7/G
look up all my ver - y clos - est friends.
F
Fm
C
E7♯9
C
E7♯9
Light, light e - nough to let it go.

Verse 2:
So set your restless heart at ease,
Take a lesson from these autumn leaves.
They waste no time waiting for the snow.
Don't argue now or you'll be late,
There's nothing to investigate.
It's light enough, light enough to let it go.
Light enough to let it go.

Remember when the scenery started fading,
I held you till you learned to walk on air.
So don't look down, the ground is gone,
There's no-one waiting anyway,
The smokey life is practiced ev'rywhere.

Stories Of The Street

Words & Music by Leonard Cohen

Am(add9)
Cmaj7
the Cad - il - lacs go creep - ing down through the
Em7
Bm
Bm7
Gmaj9
night and the poi - son gas. And I
Am(add9)
F
lean from my win - dow sill in this
G
F♯
B
old ho - tel I chose. Yes,

E
A
one hand on my su - i - cide and
E
D
one hand on the rose.
1-5.
Dmaj7/A
D6
A
Am
Am(add9)
2. I

Verse 2:
I know you've heard it's over now
And war must surely come,
The cities they are broke in half
And the middle men are gone.
But let me ask you one more time
O, children of the dusk,
These hunters who are shrieking now
Do they speak for us?

Verse 3:
And where do all these highways go
Now that we are free?
Why are the armies marching still
That were coming home to me?
O, lady with your legs so fine
O, stranger at your wheel,
You are locked into your suffering
And your pleasures are the seal.

Verse 4:
The age of lust is giving birth
But both the parents ask,
The nurse to tell them fairy tales
On both sides of the glass.
Now the infant with his cord
Is hauled in like a kite,
And one eye filled with blueprints
One eye filled with night.

Verse 5:
O come with me my little one
And we will find that farm,
And grow us grass and apples there
And keep all the animals warm.
And if by chance I wake at night
And I ask you who I am,
O, take me to the slaughterhouse
I will wait there with the lamb.

Verse 6:
With one hand on a hexagram
And one hand on a girl,
I balance on a wishing well
That all men call the world.
We are so small between the stars
So large against the sky,
And lost among the subway crowds
I try to catch your eye.

Story Of Isaac

Words & Music by Leonard Cohen

Am
F
G
F
E
blue eyes, they were shin - ing, and his voice was ver - y cold.
G
C
Said, "I've had a vi - sion, and you know I'm strong and ho - ly, I must
D
A
B
F
do what I've been told." So he start - ed up the
B♭
E
F
B♭
E
F
moun - tain, I was run - ning, he was walk - ing, and his axe

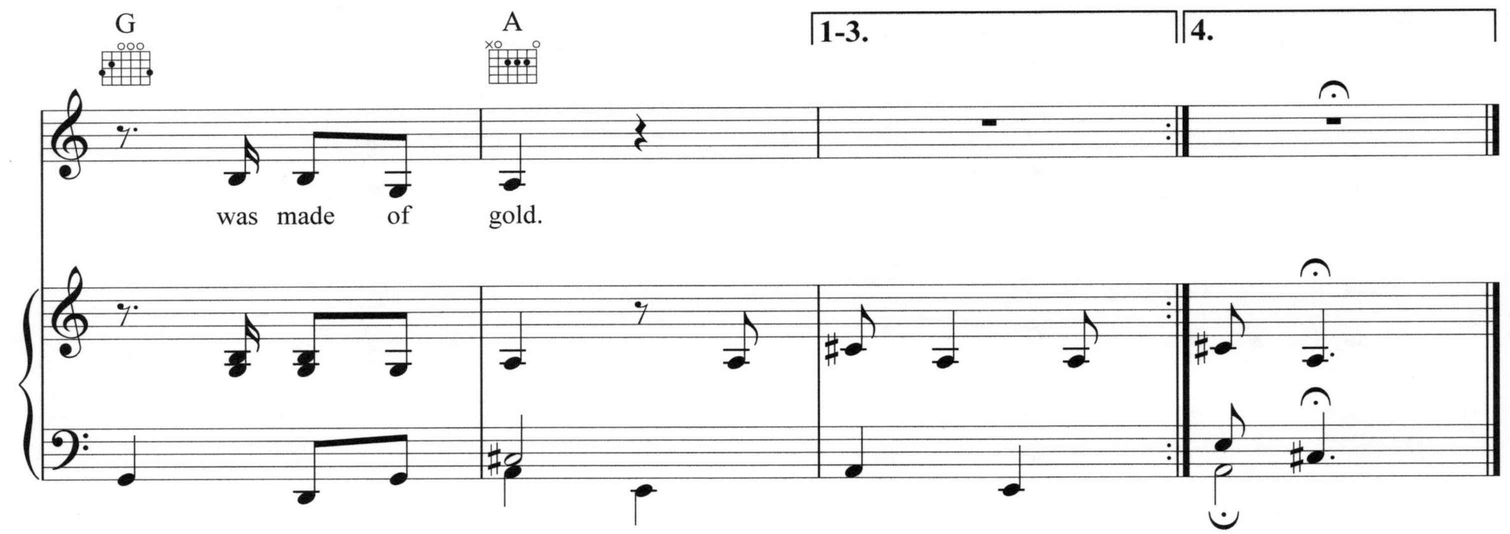

Verse 2:
The trees, they got much smaller,
The lake a lady's mirror,
We stopped to drink some wine.
Then he threw the bottle over,
Broke a minute later,
And he put his hand on mine.
Thought I saw an eagle,
But it might have been a vulture,
I never could decide.
Then my father built an altar,
He looked once behind his shoulder,
He knew I would not hide.

Verse 3:
You who build these altars now
To sacrifice these children,
You must not do it anymore.
A scheme is not a vision,
And you never have been tempted
By a demon or a god.
You who stand above them now
Your hatchets blunt and bloody,
You were not there before.
When I lay upon a mountain,
And my father's hand was trembling
With the beauty of the word.

Verse 4:
And if you call me brother now,
Forgive me if I inquire
Just according to whose plan?
When it all comes down to dust,
I will kill you if I must,
I will help you if I can.
When it all comes down to dust,
I will help you if I must,
I will kill you if I can.
And mercy on our uniform,
Man of peace or man of war,
The peacock spreads his fan.

There For You

Words & Music by Leonard Cohen & Sharon Robinson

Caug C7 Fm Fsus2/4 Caug C7
I was there for you. Don't ask me
that I thought was mine. Dressed as
Fm Fsus2/4 Caug C7 Fm Fsus2/4 Caug C7
how I know it's true, I
A - rab, dressed as Jew, a
Fm Fsus2/4 Caug C7 Fm Fsus2/4 Caug
get it now, I was there for you. I
mask of i - ron, I was there for you. Moods of
B♭m B♭sus2/4 Faug F7 B♭m B♭sus2/4 Faug F7
make my plans like I al - ways do, but when
glo - ry, moods so foul the world comes

B♭m
B♭sus2/4
Faug
F7
To Coda
B♭m
Caug
C7
I look back
I was there
for you.
I walk the
through
a blood-y towel.
Fm
Fsus2/4
Caug
C7
streets
like I
used to do,
and I
freeze
with
fear
but I'm
there
for you.
I
E♭
E♭sus2/4
D♭
E♭/D♭
6fr
3fr
4fr
see my life
in full
re - view,
it was

E♭
E♭sus2/4
E♭
E♭sus2/4
D♭
E♭/D♭
C
6fr
3fr
6fr
3fr
4fr
6fr
nev - er me,
it was al - ways you.
Fm
Fsus2/4
Caug
C7
Fm
Fsus2/4
Caug
C7
You
D♭
Fm
E♭
Fm
4fr
6fr
sent me here,
you sent me there,
D♭
Fm
E♭
Fm
4fr
6fr
break - ing things I can't re - pair,

A♭
4fr
E♭
6fr
making objects out of thought, making
B♭
C
D.S. al Coda
more of them by thinking not.
2. Eating food
Coda
B♭m
B♭sus2/4
Faug
F7
And death is old,
but it's always new,
I freeze with

B♭m B♭sus2/4 Faug F7 B♭m Caug C7
fear, and I'm there for you. I see it
Fm Fsus2/4 Caug C7 Fm Fsus2/4 Caug C7
clear, I al - ways knew it was
Fm Fsus2/4 Caug C7 Fm Fsus2/4 Caug C7
nev - er me, I was there for you. I was
E♭ E♭sus2/4 E♭ E♭sus2/4 D♭ E♭/D♭ D♭ E♭/D♭
6fr 3fr 6fr 3fr 4fr 6fr 4fr 6fr
there for you, my darl - ing one, and

E♭ E♭sus2/4 E♭ E♭sus2/4 D♭ E♭/D♭ C
6fr 3fr 6fr 3fr 4fr 6fr
by your law it all was
Fm Fsus2/4 Caug C7 Fm Fsus2/4 Caug C7
done. Don't ask me
Fsus2/4 Caug C7 Fm Fsus2/4 Caug C7
how I know it's true, I
Fsus2/4 Caug C7 Fm Fsus2/4 Caug C7
Repeat to fade
get it now, I was there for you. Don't ask me

There Is A War

Words & Music by Leonard Cohen

G
C/G
G
C/G
G
C/G
G
D
is - n't.
Why don't you come on back to the war,
C
G5
3fr
G
that's right, get in it.
Why don't you
D
C
G5
3fr
come on back to the war, it's just be - gin - ning.
Am
2. Well, I live here with a wom - an and a child, the

G
C/G
G
C/G
G
C/G
G
sit - u - a - tion makes me kind of ner - vous. Yes, I
Am
G
C/G
G
C/G
rise up from her arms, she says, "I guess you call this love, I call it serv - ice."
G
C/G
G
D
C
Why don't you come on back to the war? Don't be a tou - rist.
G
C/G
G
C/G
G
C/G
G
D
Why don't you come on back to the war

C
G5
3fr
before it hurts us?
Why don't you
D
C
G
C/G
G
C/G
come on back to the war? Let's all get nerv-ous.
G
C/G
G
Am
3. You can-not stand what I've be-come, you much pre-
G
C/G
G
C/G
G
C/G
G
-fer the gen-tle-man I was be-fore.
It was so

Am
eas - y to de - feat, I was so eas - y to con - trol, I did - n't e - ven know there was a
G C/G G C/G G C/G G D
war. Why don't you come on back to the war?
C G C/G G C/G G C/G G
Don't be em - bar - rassed. Why don't you
D C G C/G G C/G
come on back to the war? You can still get mar - ried.

G
C/G
G
Am
4. There is a war be - tween the rich and poor, a
war be-tween the man and the wom - an.
There is a
war be - tween the left and right, a war be - tween the black and white, a
war be-tween the odd and the e - ven.
Why don't you

D C G C/G G C/G
come on back_ to the war?_ Pick up your ti - ny bur - den.
G C/G G D C
Why don't you come on back_ to the war?_ Let's all_ get e - ven._
G5 3fr D
_ Why don't you come on back_ to the war,_
C G5 3fr
_ can't you hear_ me speak- ing?_

Tonight Will Be Fine

Words & Music by Leonard Cohen

E
A
am too thin and your love is too vast. But I
D
A
know from your eyes, and I
D
A
know from your smile, that to -
D
A
- night will be fine, will be fine, will be

Verse 2:
I choose the rooms that I live in with care.
The windows are small and the walls must be bare.
There's only one bed and there's only one prayer.
And I listen all night for your step on the stair.

But I know *etc.*

Verse 3:
Sometimes I see her undressing for me.
She's the soft naked lady love meant her to be.
And she's moving her body so brave and so free.
If I've got to remember, that's a fine memory.

And I know *etc.*

The Traitor

Words & Music by Leonard Cohen

A
G
A7
D
judg - es watched us from the oth - er side.
2. I
D
G
D
told my moth - er, "Moth - er, I must leave you.
Pre -
G
D
-serve my room but do not shed a tear.
Should
F#7
Bm
G
D
ru - mours of a shab - by end - ing reach you,
it was

A
G
A7
D
1, 2.
(to next strain)
half my fault and half the at - mos - phere."
But the
3.
Fine
D
G
D
rose I sick - ened with a scar - let fev - er.
And the swan I tempt - ed with a sense of
G
D
F#7
Bm
shame.
She said at last I was her fin - est

Verse 4:
The judges said, "You missed it by a fraction,
Rise up and brace your troops for the attack.
The dreamers ride against the men of action,
Oh, see the men of action falling back."

Verse 5:
But I lingered on her thighs a fatal moment,
I kissed her lips as though I thirsted still.
My falsity, it stung me like a hornet,
The poison sank and it paralysed my will.

Verse 6:
I could not move to warn all the younger soldiers
That they had been deserted from above.
So on battlefields from here to Barcelona
I'm listed with the enemies of love.

Verse 7:
And long ago she said "I must be leaving,
Ah but keep my body here to lie upon.
You can move it up and down and when I'm sleeping,
Run some wire through that rose and wind the swan."

Verse 8:
So daily I renew my idle duty,
I touch her here and there, I know my place.
I kiss her open mouth and I praise her beauty,
And people call me "traitor" to my face.

True Love Leaves No Traces

Words & Music by Leonard Cohen & Phil Spector

D7
Gm
3fr
C7
hill, so my bod - y leaves no scar on
air, so your head up - on my breast, so my
F
you, and nev-er will.
hand up - on your hair.
Through win-dows in the
And man - y nights en -
Am/E
Am7♭5/E♭
dark, the chil - dren come, the chil - dren
- dure with - out a moon, with - out a star,
D7
Gm
3fr
go like ar - rows with no
so we will en -

C7
3fr
F
F/E
F/D
tar - gets, like shack - les made of snow.
-dure when one is gone far.
C7
F
True love leaves no trac - es, if you and I are
one; it's lost in our em - brac - es like
stars a - gainst the sun.

1.
2.
Gm
3fr
C7/G
C9
C7/G
C9
2. As a
F
Am/E
2° poco a poco dim
Am7♭5/E♭
D7
Gm
3fr
C7
F
1.
2.
D.S. to fade
F/E
F/D

Why Don't You Try

Words & Music by Leonard Cohen

F♯
G
D
-sion? Do you real - ly need his heart for your throne? Do you
A
G7
A
need his la - bor for you ba - by? Do you need his beast for the
G7
A
G7
bone? Do you need to hold a leash to be a la - dy? I
D
G
D/A
G
D/A
know you're gon - na make it, make it on your

Verse 2:
Why don't your try to forget him?
Just open up your dainty little hand.
You know this life is filled with many sweet companions,
Many satisfying one-night stands.

Do you want to be the ditch around a tower?
Do you want to be the moonlight in his cave?
Do you want to give your blessing to his power
As he goes whistling past his daddy, past his daddy's grave?

Verse 3:
I'd like to take you to the ceremony,
Well, that is if I remember the way.
You see Jack and Jill, they're gonna join their misery,
I'm afraid it's time for everyone to pray.

You can see they've finally taken cover,
They're willing, yeah, they're willing to obey.
Their vows are difficult, they're for each other
So let nobody put a loophole, a loophole in their way.

Winter Lady

Words & Music by Leonard Cohen

Amaj7
D
I'm just a sta - tion on your
C
D
A
D
way, I know I am not your lov - er.
1st and 2nd time to next strain
Fine
A
D
D
Well,
D/A
Am7
I lived with a child of snow

Verse 2:
She used to wear her hair like you,
Except when she was sleeping.
And then she'd weave it on a loom
Of smoke and gold and breathing.

And why are you so quiet now,
Standing there in the doorway?
You chose your journey long before
You came upon this highway.

Trav'ling lady, stay awhile
Until the night is over.
I'm just a station on your way,
I know I'm not your lover.

The Window

Words & Music by Leonard Cohen

F
G
C
spear of the age in your side.
Lost in the
G
F
G
ra - ges of fra - grance,
lost in the rags of re -
C
G
- morse.
Lost in the waves of the sick - ness
F
G
C
G/B
Am7
that loos - ens the high sil - ver nerves.
Oh,

G
cho - sen love, oh, fro - zen love, oh,
F Em Dm C G/B Am7
tan - gle of mat - ter and ghost. Oh,
G
darl - ing of an - gels, de - mons and saints and the
F Em Dm C G/B Am7
whole bro - ken - heart - ed host. Gen - tle this

Verse 2:
And come forth from the cloud of unknowing
And kiss the cheek of the moon.
The New Jerusalem glowing,
Why tarry all night in the ruin.

And leave no word of discomfort,
And leave no observer to mourn,
But climb on your tears and be silent
Like a rose on its ladder of thorns.

Oh chosen love, oh frozen love *etc*.

Verse 3:
Then lay your rose on the fire,
The fire give up to the sun.
The sun give over to splendour
In the arms of the High Holy One.

For the Holy One dreams of a letter,
Dreams of a letter's death.
Oh bless thee continuous stutter
Of the word being made into flesh.

Oh chosen love, oh frozen love *etc*.

You Know Who I Am

Words & Music by Leonard Cohen

F
C
I am the dis - tance you put be - tween all of the
B♭
D7/A
G
mo - ments that we will be. You
F
C
F
know who I am, you've stared at the
C
F
C
sun. Well, I am the one who loves

Verse 2:
Sometimes I need you naked,
Sometimes I need you wild.
I need you to carry my children in,
And I need you to kill a child.

You know who I am *etc.*

Verse 3:
If you should ever track me down,
I will surrender there.
And I'll leave with you one broken man
Whom I'll teach you to repair.

You know who I am *etc.*

Verse 4:
I cannot follow you, my love,
You cannot follow me.
I am the distance you put between
All the moments that we will be.

You know who I am *etc.*

1 2 3 4 5 6 7 8 9